"Every block of stone has a statue inside it and it is the task of the sculptor to discover it."
—Michelangelo

"My first notebook entry on what might have been a working transistor was, as I recall, late 1939. Then the war intervened."
—William Shockley, Nobel Laureate

"The advent of digital technology is going to have a huge impact on the world. The degree of the impact is just going to pervade culture in the same way as the Gutenberg press or the Industrial Revolution or the invention of fire."
—Doug Engelbart, Inventor of the computer mouse

"Find something you're passionate about that you really believe in. This is not a job; this becomes part of you."
—Dan Warmenhoven, CEO Network Appliance

"There was a competition between Bill Hewlett and Myrl Stearns about who could climb the sandstone walls of Stanford's Inner Quad higher. They climbed with their fingernails and climbed up to the top, and Bill Hewlett, I think, won."

—Ed Ginzton, Founder, Varian Associates

"The Renaissance was an entrepreneurial movement so that at root Silicon Valley today and the Medici blossoming of trade in the 15th Century are exactly analogous."
—Lisa Jardine, Professor of Renaissance Studies, Queen Mary, University of London.

"We had 30 days credit on the parts and we built a computer and delivered it to a store and got paid in cash in 10 days so we were able to pay off the loan on the parts."
—Steve Wozniak, Founder Apple Computer

"The creative genius is what makes it all go. The rest of us, as I see it, are enablers."
—Jerry Sanders, founder AMD

"If we have a good idea, a reasonable business plan, and a clearly definable market, then there is a possibility of success."
—Fred Hoar, early Apple marketing director

"Let's make it so that anyone with a beer in one hand could play the game, and that was really how we structured it, and that was Pong."
—Nolan Bushnell, Founder Atari

"Silicon Valley is not so much a place for scientific innovation. It is a great place for application innovation."
—David Lam, Founder Lam Research

"THERE WERE FOUR OF US THAT PAID $50,000 FOR ABOUT 50 BOXES OF STUFF AND WE LEFT HEWLETT-PACKARD TO SET UP SHOP IN THE OLD THEATER BUILDING IN LOS ALTOS."
—CHUCK TRIMBLE, FOUNDER TRIMBLE NAVIGATION

"It's hard to realize just how naive we were about the magnitude of the business we were getting into."
—Gordon Moore, Founder of Fairchild Semiconductor and Intel. A member of Shockley's Traitorous Eight.

"Talk of nothing but business, and dispatch that business quickly."
—Aldus Manutius,

"All those things have given me the greatest satisfaction and contentment because they are not only for the honor of God but are likewise for my own remembrance. For fifty years, I have done nothing else but earn money and spend money; and it became clear that spending money gives me greater pleasure than earning it."
—Cosimo de' Medici

"I have been impressed with the urgency of doing. Knowing is not enough; we must apply. Being willing is not enough; we must do."
—Leonardo da Vinci

"I think Silicon Valley has a unique culture of believing almost anything's possible."
—Larry Ellison, Founder Oracle

"Our primary interest was to get something that would bring some money in the door. We tried all kinds of things. We tried building diathermy machines, shocking machines to make people lose weight, a device to tune harmonicas, air conditioning controls ..."
—Bill Hewlett, Founder Hewlett-Packard

"The infrastructure in Silicon Valley is something people don't talk about, but I don't know of another place where you get anything you want made over night out of anything, painted any color or plated with anything. And, you do it off the back of a book of matches."
—Robert Graham, Founder Intel

"We didn't realize as researchers how important it was to follow our inventions through all the way to the point of building a product. And how hard it is to sell new ideas whether we are within a company or to the outside world."
—Charles Geschke, Founder Adobe Systems

SILICON VALLEY:
110 YEAR RENAISSANCE

Publisher: John R. McLaughlin
Authors: John McLaughlin, Leigh Weimers, Ward Winslow
Project Director: Gina Woolf
Art Director: Keith Costas
Managing Editor: Sally McBurney
Corporate History Editor: Carol Whiteley

First Edition

Library of Congress Catalog Card Number: 2007935441
Winslow, Wardell V., 1927-2000
McLaughlin, John R., 1949-
Weimers, Leigh A., 1935-

Silicon Valley: 110 Year Renaissance
196 pages
8.5 x 11 inch format
Includes bibliography and index
ISBN 096492174X

Published in Palo Alto, California USA
Printed on recycled paper in Hong Kong

The Santa Clara Valley Historical Association would like to thank the following companies for their generous support as Premier Sponsors:

We would also like to give special thanks to the following companies for their support:

Abbott, Adobe Systems, AMD, Applied Materials, Ariba, Inc., Atmel Corporation, BAE Systems, Communications & Power Industries, Inc., Cornish & Carey Commercial/ONCOR International, Covad Communications Group, Inc., Cypress Semiconductor Corporation, E*TRADE Financial, Intel Corporation, IXYS Corporation, KLA-Tencor Corporation, Komag Incorporated, Lam Research Foundation, Linear Technology Corporation, LSI Corporation, Maxim Integrated Products, Inc., McAfee, Inc., MIPS Technologies, Inc., NVIDIA Corporation, NXP Semiconductors, O.C. McDonald, Oracle Corporation, Palm, Inc., PMC-Sierra Ltd., Ropers Majeski Kohn & Bentley, SanDisk, Inc., SRI International, Silicon Storage Technology, Inc., Symantec Corporation, Tyco Electronics, Varian Medical Systems, Vishay Siliconix, Wilson Sonsini Goodrich & Rosati Foundation, Xilinx, Inc., and Zoran Corporation.

Incipit liber bresich quē nos genesim
dicim9. IN principio creauit deus celū
et terram. Terra autem erat inanis et
vacua: et tenebre erāt sup faciē abissi:
et sps dūi ferebat sup aquas. Dixitqꝫ
deus. fiat lux. Et facta ē lux. Et vidit
deus lucem qꝫ esset bona: ꝫ diuisit lucē
a tenebris. Appellauitqꝫ lucem diem: ꝫ
tenebras nocten. factūqꝫ est vespe et
mane dies vnus. Dixit qꝫ deus. fiat
firmamentū in medio aquaꝝ: ꝫ diui-
dat aquas ab aquis. Et fecit deus firmamentū: diuisitqꝫ aquas que erāt
sub firmameto ab hijs qꝫ erant sup
firmamentū: et factū ē ita. Vocauitqꝫ
deus firmamentū celū: ꝫ factū ē vespe
et mane dies secūd9. Dixit vero deus.
Congregentur aque que sub celo sūt in
locū vnū: ꝫ appareat arida. Et factū ē
ita. Et vocauit deus aridam terram:
congregationesqꝫ aquaꝝ appellauit
maria. Et vidit deus qꝫ esset bonū: et
ait. Germinet terra herbā virentem et
facientē semen: ꝫ lignū pomifeꝝ faciēs
fructū iuxta genus suū: cui9 semen in
semetipo sit sup terrā. Et factū ē ita. Et
protulit terra herbā virente ꝫ faciente
semē iuxta genus suū: lignūqꝫ faciēs
fructū ꝫ habes vnūqdqꝫ semente sedm
speciē suā. Et vidit deus qꝫ esset bonū:
et factū est vespe et mane dies tercius.
Dixit qꝫ autē deus. fiant luminaria
in firmameto celi: ꝫ diuidāt diem ac
nocten: ꝫ sint in signa ꝫ tpa et dies ꝫ
annos: ut luceāt in firmameto celi et
illuminēt terrā. Et factū ē ita. Fecitqꝫ
deus duo luminaria magna: luminare
maius ut pesset diei: et luminare min9
ut pesset nocti: ꝫ stellas: ꝫ posuit eas in
firmameto celi ut lucerēt sup terrā: et

pessent diei ac nocti: ꝫ diuiderent lucē
ac tenebras. Et vidit de9 qꝫ esset bonū:
et factū ē vespe ꝫ mane dies quartus.
Dixit etiā de9. Producāt aque reptile
anime viuentis ꝫ volatile super terrā:
sub firmameto celi. Creauitqꝫ deus cete
grandia: et omne aiam viuentē atqꝫ
motabile quā produxerāt aque i species
suas: ꝫ omne volatile sedm gen9 suū.
Et vidit deus qꝫ esset bonū: benedixitqꝫ
eis dicens. Crescite ꝫ multiplicamini: ꝫ
replete aquas maris: auesqꝫ multipli-
cent sup terrā. Et factū ē vespe ꝫ mane:
dies quitus. Dixit quoqꝫ deus. Pro-
ducat terra aiam viuente in genē suo:
iumenta ꝫ reptilia: ꝫ bestias terre sedm
species suas. factūqꝫ ē ita. Et fecit de9
bestias terre iuxta species suas: iumenta ꝫ omne reptile terre i genere suo. Et
vidit deus qꝫ esset bonū: et ait. facia-
mus hoiem ad ymagine ꝫ silitudinē
nostrā: ꝫ presit piscibꝫ maris: et volatilibꝫ celi ꝫ bestijs vniuerseqꝫ terre: omniqꝫ
reptili qd mouetur i terra. Et creauit
deus hoiem ad ymagine ꝫ silitudinē
suā: ad ymagine dei creauit illū: ma-
sculū ꝫ feminā creauit eos. Benedixit
qꝫ illis deus: ꝫ ait. Crescite ꝫ multiplicamini ꝫ replete terrā: et sbicite eā: et dia-
mini piscibꝫ maris: et volatilibꝫ celi:
et vniuersis animātibꝫ que mouent
sup terrā. Dixitqꝫ de9. Ecce dedi vobis
omne herbā afferente semen sup terrā:
et vniūsa ligna que hūt in semetipis
semente genis sui: ut sint vobis i escā:
ꝫ cunctis aiantibꝫ terre: oiqꝫ volucri
celi ꝫ vniuersis qꝫ mouetur in terra: ꝫ i
quibꝫ est anima viues: ut habeāt ad
vescendū. Et factū est ita. Viditqꝫ deus
cuncta que fecerat: ꝫ erāt valde bona.

Table of Contents

Preface

The constellation known today as Silicon Valley represents the choicest achievements of America's high technology through the 20th Century and now into the 21st — a period during which the United States surged to world technological leadership and poured out inventions, innovations, and developments in a volume unprecedented in history, either in quality or quantity.

The purpose of this book is to collect and pass on to new generations an understanding of how this phenomenon came to be. Thus, the Santa Clara Valley Historical Association has sought to explain the events and conditions that prepared the locality for its present role, to set down the broad outlines of what happened both before and after 1970, when Silicon Valley got its nickname, and to list what appear today to be the key inventions. In this book, the text of the chronological chapters is interlaced with the histories of companies that started operations here in the same eras. Read together, these chronicles will, we hope, give the reader a general picture of the making of Silicon Valley.

In saying so, we must add that the picture does not include every detail we or others might wish. It is not exhaustive, not complete. Indeed, a history that purports to cover a subject as broad and diverse as this one almost up to its date of publication cannot be complete. Even if it could, the notorious difficulty of assessing the historic import of recent events would render interpretation chancy, at best.

So not every event is reported, not every company is mentioned, not every issue is explored in depth. Other authors have illuminated certain facets brilliantly; their works will be found listed in a bibliography. Neither do we claim to be teachers explaining each wondrous product or principle.

In conducting scores of interviews with company founders, inventors, engineers, entrepreneurs, venture capitalists, scientists, professors, and others with an insider's understanding of a technology, a company, or the Valley itself, our questions have tended to follow a consistent pattern. We have asked what motivated these individuals, when their interest in science or technology began, how they went about forming their companies, what attitude they took toward the risk of failure inherent in creating a start-up, which hurdles were the most challenging to leap, and how their enterprises grew. We have sought to bring out why they deemed Silicon Valley the right place for their firms, and what they would advise young persons considering careers as entrepreneurs or creators in high technology.

Most of these interviews were filmed. This database has provided much of the material for the DVD that accompanies this book and may later be available in future forms of electronic storage. It constitutes an exceptional (and almost impossible to duplicate) record of the founders and pioneers telling their stories, animated by their distinctive facial expressions and tone of voice. The book does not begin to encompass the entire content of these interviews, or the personalities of their subjects, but we hope it does derive some flavor from them, for they are a remarkable group of human beings.

The Palo Alto Historical Association originally served as a cosponsor of the Santa Clara Valley Historical Association in this project, lending its name and the run of photographic files. Steven Staiger, PAHA's historian and a City of Palo Alto reference librarian, has been of great assistance. Gail Woolley, a past PAHA president and former mayor of Palo Alto, was instrumental in shaping our endeavor, as were PAHA presidents Crystal D. Gamage and Judy Leahy. Susan Bright Winn, a past PAHA president, worked with exceptional devotion on transcribing interview tapes.

We are indebted also to Donald Koijane, president of the Perham Foundation, Inc., for access to its photographic collection and for his counsel, particularly regarding aspects of radio. The Perham Foundation Electronics Museum now is housed at the San Jose Historical Museum.

At Stanford University, former Dean of Engineering James Gibbons has been of great assistance. So have Margaret Kimball and Linda Long at the Special Collections Department of Green Library, and Henry Lowood, the bibliographer for history of science and technology collections at the Stanford University Libraries. We are grateful for the help of the Stanford Office of News and Publications.

At the California History Center at De Anza College, Lisa Christiansen, librarian of the Louis Stocklmeir Regional History Library, assisted with both file research and photos.

At the *San Jose Mercury News*, Executive Editor Jerry Ceppos, Managing Editor David Yarkin, Candace Turtle, and Library Director Gary Lance arranged for us to use many historic photographs.

Santa Clara Valley Historical Association board members, James Harrison, Jim Hudspeth and Sheri Midgely helped shape the project. Others who labored to bring it to life included Josh Wagner, Paul Salcedo and Alice Kleeman for her transcription skills.

For legal counsel we are grateful to Tom Alderman. Those who acted as sounding boards and advisers include: Kevin Burr, Tom Hummel, Jim McCormick, Jill Amen, Richard Millward, Russell Kostner, David Wong, Peter Lonsky, Robert Metcalfe, Linda Metcalfe, Helene Scott, Bill Woolf, Jack Drucker, Gary Simpson, Arielle Rothenberg and Daniel Rothenberg.

Walter Cronkite was thoroughly professional and gracious when working with us on the first PBS documentary, *Silicon Valley: A 100 Year Renaissance*, as was Leonard Nimoy on narrating the second documentary, *Silicon Valley: 110 Year Renaissance*. Dennis McNalley of The Grateful Dead arranged the use of musical excerpts as well as an interview with the late Jerry Garcia.

Although these and many other individuals have lent a hand in advancing this project, the accuracy of this book is strictly the responsibility of our staff. We sincerely hope it will be useful in educating the world — and especially students — about the making of Silicon Valley and its continuing development into the new millennium.

Ward Winslow
Palo Alto, California
September 30, 1995

Leigh Weimers
Los Gatos, California
June 22, 2007

Introduction

Silicon Valley is descended from the imagination.

Other economic powerhouses in the world's economy have been formed out of crossroads, rivers, and deep-water ports. Other powers have been forged by military objectives, defensible boundaries and easy access to the earth's valuable resources. But Silicon Valley has no door on its geographic position, no roof on its character. The allegiance of most people here is to innovation, to the right to take risks, to exalt the successful entrepreneur and to offer an understanding hand to those who failed. Boundaries here are best drawn by connected intellects, not by place names.

There are certain periods in history when discoveries and events, both political and in technology, create a window when civilization has the opportunity to leap forward. One of these was a convergence of events and inventions that spurred on an age of discovery. We know this age as the Renaissance. The underlying event was the advent of the Black Death, the plague. The decimation of cheap labor led to labor saving innovations and to the crucial inventions. The primary advancements during the Renaissance were the printing press, the compass and gunpowder. It was the printing press and subsequently, the development of small affordable books that created the first information revolution. Gunpowder and the decimation of the labor force changed the political landscape from a feudal society. The compass enabled the great voyages to discover new worlds.

The Renaissance was a time of invention, entrepreneurial accomplishments and exploration — very similar to what has occurred in Silicon Valley. The historical periods are remarkably alike.

The convergence of the personal computer, router technology that allows different computer platforms to communicate and the end of the Cold War, which prompted the democratization of the Internet, all were crucial to the new Information Revolution.

Where this new age will take humanity is largely in the minds of inventors and entrepreneurs. While the earth's horizon looks ever darker as a result of our long history of damaging the environment — there is hope to reverse global warming — in the culture we know as Silicon Valley.

John R. McLaughlin
November 1, 2007
Palo Alto, California, USA

Chapter 1: The Making of Silicon Valley—An Overview

Bank of Palo Alto, 1911

Strong waves of creative energy have flowed in recent decades from a place known as "Silicon Valley," encircling — and changing — the world. How it happened is the subject of this book.

The phenomenon known since the 1970s as Silicon Valley can be traced to origins in the 1890s when Leland Stanford established a university at Palo Alto and urged that its students not only gain knowledge but be able to apply their learning in the real world. Pioneer professors, especially in the sciences and engineering, took Senator Stanford's cue and collaborated with nearby industries from the outset.

As the 20th century began, wireless radio captured public attention, soon after introduction of the telegraph and the telephone. The wonder of Morse code or the human voice riding mysterious air waves excited adults and youths alike. Palo Alto became an early test bed for radio experiment. Later it became the locale for development of continuous-wave transmission powered by arc generators, thanks to engineer-entrepreneur Cyril Elwell. Elwell employed a radio research team including Lee de Forest, who in 1906 had invented a three-element vacuum tube in New York. In 1912 the team discovered that the tube, which de Forest called the audion, could be rigged as an amplifier. This was a major breakthrough. It was first exploited in long-distance telephony, then in radio, and later in other tube-powered devices, such as radar, television, and computer systems, over a span of about 40 years.

Radio took root on the San Francisco Peninsula. In San Jose, Charles Herrold began the first regularly scheduled radio broadcasts in 1912. In Palo Alto, the Federal Telegraph Company established by Elwell created ocean-spanning networks, supplying U.S. Navy communications during World War I. Many of Stanford University's electrical engineering graduates worked at Federal for a time. Tube-making companies were founded on the Peninsula, and a technical community built up. At Stanford, Frederick Terman became the leading academic authority on radio engineering.

At Stanford, physics professor William Hansen developed insights that were applied by the Varian brothers in the klystron tube and later in linear accelerators, which proved useful in smashing atoms and treating cancer. A generation of microwave engineers emerged, helping to win World War II and afterward exploiting television and long-range communications.

In the postwar years, Hewlett-Packard Company became the dominant local electronics company, developing measuring equipment, scientific instruments, a program-

Palo Alto Circle

1769	**1776**	**1849**	**1850**	**1864**	**1876**	**1888**
Spaniards camp near S.F. Bay.	*Pueblo of San Jose founded.*	*Gold Rush populates California.*	*U.S. admits California as 31st state.*	*Peninsula railroad is completed.*	*Alexander Graham Bell invents the telephone.*	*Heinrich Hertz demonstrates radio waves.*

mable calculator, and ultimately computers, printers and other peripherals. HP also served as a management school. Droves of its graduates became mainstays of other companies.

Meanwhile, in 1947 a Bell Labs team led by William Shockley invented the transistor, which after years of development would replace the electron tube. Shockley returned to Palo Alto, his boyhood home, to commercialize the transistor. Eight crack young scientists and engineers he had recruited as assistants broke away and formed Fairchild Semiconductors. Led by Robert Noyce, they invented a practicable integrated circuit and delved into the chemical magic of planar processes. Solid state physics took hold, ultimately chasing away most Peninsula microwave development. From crude ICs that many companies built on their own for a time, the art developed more and more specialties.

Sand Hill Road 1904

IBM's invention of the random-access memory system in San Jose energized the infant computer industry and grew an entire new branch, disk drives.

The Cold War and the space race gave big boosts to electronics and aerospace companies. Semiconductor development surged. Then Fairchild Semiconductor all but self-destructed. That explosion left dozens, nay scores, of glowing embers in the Valley.

Intel was one of the companies formed by Fairchild refugees. Intel pioneered the art of putting read-only computer memory on chips, and then scored the most important breakthrough of the latter 20th century, the creation of the microprocessor. Ted Hoff proposed the architecture and Federico Faggin made it work. These computers on a chip, growing ever more powerful, at length enabled Silicon Valley's microcomputer industry to dethrone the Boston area minicomputer companies. The advent of the personal computer, pioneered by young Steve Wozniak and Steve Jobs, also was a vital element in the computer revolution.

The phenomenal development of semiconductors and electronics fed upon itself. Ambitious engineers, entrepreneurs, and managers began to see Silicon Valley as a mecca. They came sometimes directly to industry, sometimes with a stop at Stanford or the University of California at Berkeley for a Ph.D. or an MBA — to learn and to look for a new wave to ride.

Opportunity could be read in the many personal and corporate successes. The local climate was benign, the culture open and exciting. The Valley was experiencing a wave of intellectual and creative energy at least the equal of any in the European Renaissance four to five centuries earlier. Investors were attracted, and a venture capital community gained heft.

Semiconductor manufacturers at first made their own processing equipment, but as processes became more complex, equipment manufacturers took over that job, became a separate industry, and eventually automated their clever systems.

Research may be more advanced in Silicon Valley than anywhere else, and not only in the universities and SRI International (a precedent-setting applied research facility), not only in the government's Ames Research Center and Lawrence Livermore Laboratories, not only in such world-renowned industrial research centers as IBM's and HP's and Lockheed Missiles & Space Company's and the Xerox Palo Alto Research Center, but in almost every high technology company. As for development, industries have honed their timetables, telescoping the time required to bring a product to market — a better quality product than the one it replaced.

1891	**1901**	**1906**	**1912**	**1917**	**1927**	**1937**
Stanford University classes open.	*Marconi sends trans-Atlantic radio signal.*	*Earthquake, fire devastate San Francisco.*	*Audion tubes amplify fly's footsteps.*	*Palo Alto firm supplies WWI Navy radios.*	*Fred Terman begins to teach at Stanford.*	*Varian brothers build klystron at Stanford.*

Stanford's First Graduation

Management processes created in the Valley are likewise noteworthy. Hundreds of new techniques and styles have blossomed, and some of them are exemplary. Law practice relating to high technology has been drastically altered. Marketing communications specialists have broken new ground. Desktop publishing arose in the Valley, as did the quantum jump in movie special effects powered by 3-D computing.

Another industry, biotechnology, sprang from discoveries of gene-splicing and gene-cloning at the great Bay Area universities.

Part of what makes Silicon Valley tick is the sharing of knowledge. Boundaries that once isolated companies or academic departments are breached not only in industry but on campus, creating cross-fertilization and new synergy. For example, visionaries have applied fast computers to new kinds of drug research, and advances in lasers to new medical devices. Many a technical or management bottleneck was broken by the sharing of information and experiences, usually not directly with a competitor but with a peer or a mentor.

Primary dissemination of knowledge occurs at the universities and at exceptional four-year colleges and two-year community colleges. San Jose State University is renowned for supplying high technology companies with more engineers than come from all other colleges combined.

Even companies accustomed to doing everything "in house" learned that that was no longer necessary. The Valley had grown an infrastructure. This supporting network of suppliers and service providers allows companies to focus on their special skills and hire help to fill the gaps. They get quick service on components, design, and other orders.

Riches have rewarded the Valley's output. To some participants, money is a great motivator; others thrive on the sheer excitement of helping to create something new and different. Even after 25 or 30 years of start-up companies granting stock options, initial public offerings still create instant multimillionaires at high tech companies. Beyond the lifestyles it enables, money is an essential fuel for such companies, for the cost of building plants and ramping new production have soared while the interval between new products has shortened.

"Silicon Valley" is a term coined by a trade press editor in 1971. Insiders who use the term mean more than a place, they mean a culture too. The heartland runs from San Carlos and Redwood City through Menlo Park, Palo Alto, Mountain View, Sunnyvale, Cupertino, Santa Clara, San Jose, and Milpitas. Strong outposts are in Fremont, Hayward, San Leandro, Emeryville, Berkeley, San Ramon, Pleasanton, San Rafael, South San Francisco, Scotts Valley, and Monterey. Given today's digitized home offices and telecommuting (or the local tradition of starting a business in one's garage), power centers might also be found in such lush foothills residential towns as Hillsborough, Woodside, Portola Valley, Atherton, the Los Altos area, Saratoga, Monte Sereno, and Los Gatos.

Not every Silicon Valley leader views its burgeoning as a renaissance. However, most do, and at present they can see no end to it. Technologies will inevitably change, but they expect the entrepreneurial and creative drive to carry far into the 21st century, and perhaps much farther.

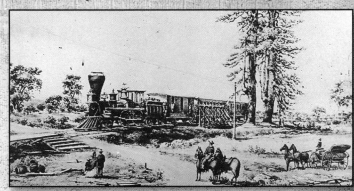

Railroad at Palo Alto's Tall Tree

1939
Bill Hewlett &
Dave Packard
start company.

1941
Wounded U.S.
enters WWII.

1946
SRI founded
to do research
for the West.

1952
IBM sets up
laboratory in
San Jose.

1953
Varian first in
Stanford Indus-
trial Park.

1956
Lockheed moves
division to
Sunnyvale.

1957
Soviet Union
orbits Sputnik.

Silicon Valley Achievements

Silicon Valley's copious outpouring of inventions, scientific discoveries, adaptations, and developments makes a long list. The Valley's contributions to civilization include, in part:

Long distance high-voltage transmission, the amplifying vacuum tube, the first commercial radio broadcast, long distance continuous-wave radio transmissions, mobile radio systems development, the klystron tube and microwave radar, electronic measuring devices, nuclear induction applications, the X-ray microscope, traveling-wave tube development, silicon crystal-growing, programmable hand-held calculators, videotape and VCRs, development of the junction transmitter, linear accelerators for particle physics research and cancer treatment.

Swept-back aircraft wings, nuclear magnetic resonance, random access computer storage; disk drives, integrated circuits, planar processes, lasers, semiconductor large-scale integrated memory, silicon gate arrays, microprocessors, light-emitting diodes (LEDs), personal computers, open-heart surgery, ink-jet printing, high resolution aerial photography, spacecraft heat shields, batch processing of micromachined devices, gene-cloning and gene-splicing.

Video games, silicon compilers, automated semiconductor manufacturing equipment, field programmable gate arrays, prodigious advances in artificial limbs and sensory aids, robotics, genetic engineering, satellite technology, 3-D computing, and a host of other wonders.

The Stanford Laureates are joined by a Swedish Nobel Laureate, visiting from Sweden, and by the Swedish and Norwegian Consuls General in San Francisco.

They are, from left, upper row: Bill Sharpe, Michael Bishop, Paul Berg, Burton Richter, Arno Penzias, Barbro Osher, Consul General of Sweden, and Are-Jostein Norheim, Consul General of Norway.

Bottom row: Arthur Kornberg, Richard Taylor, Charles Townes, Arvid Carlsson (Sweden), Martin Perl and George Akerlof.

1958
NASA created;
Stanford prof
proposes laser.

1959
Noyce-led 8
build integrated
circuit.

1966
Particle physics
research starts
at SLAC.

1969
U.S. astronauts
first to land
on the Moon.

Chapter 2: Leland Stanford Founds a University Dedicated to Making Its Graduates Useful to the World

Leland Stanford

Two centuries ago, the Santa Clara Valley and the San Francisco Bay lay almost untouched by human endeavor. The thin population of Costaño Indians, inhabitants for many thousand years, had walked softly on the land, leaving little but shell mounds as traces of their hunter-gatherer culture. The oak-studded valley floor, with willow thickets near the shore and dense chaparral edging the foothills and the timbered mountains, showed only the creations of nature.

European explorers came starting in 1769—Spanish soldiers and Franciscan padres. Slowly they built presidios (army bases) and a chain of missions. The missions became hubs for agriculture and for attempts to convert and domesticate the indigenous "heathens" to Christianity. Farming proved to be the more successful activity.

Late in 1777, California's first civil settlement was established in the heart of the Santa Clara Valley—*el Pueblo de San José de Guadalupé*. Frequent flooding led to the town's relocation away from the river in 1797; even then the initial count of 66 settlers had not doubled. Early in the 1820s, Mexico broke away from Spain and began to rule in Alta California. The jurisdiction of the San Jose *ayuntamiento* or town council spread northward into San Mateo and Alameda counties. After control of the missions passed from church to civil authorities in the mid-1830s, some of Mission Santa Clara's grazing lands in the present Mountain View-Palo Alto area were granted to individual owners.

In the 1839-1844 period, San Jose wrested from San Francisco the honor of being *la cabrera del partido*, or capital of the district. But that was not to last, for San Francisco was ideally suited for water transportation in the prime of the sailing ship, and about 1845 its population began to swell. Just before the Gold Rush, the town founded in 1835 had grown to 200 shacks and adobes inhabited by about 800 whites.

In 1846, American Capt. John B. Montgomery sailed the sloop of war Portsmouth into the bay, landed with sailors and marines and raised the U.S. flag in the plaza. The 1849 Gold Rush gradually filled San Francisco harbor with deserted ships, their crews having rushed to the diggings. But it was not the miners who got rich—those who fed, provisioned, and otherwise catered to them did.

Rapid growth helped win California statehood in 1850, and San Jose enjoyed a brief time as the first state capital. But valley and Peninsula land remained in farming and ranching, and thus stayed open, generally in large tracts. Logging stripped the mountains to the west to supply San Francisco's ravenous appetite for building materials.

In 1863, an upstate New York-born lawyer who had prospered as a merchant supplying miners was elected governor. Leland Stanford served for only two years, but long afterward was esteemed as the "Civil War governor" who had exerted his powers to keep the state in the Union and aid President Lincoln. He and three compatriots, Charles Crocker, Mark Hopkins, and Colis P. Huntington, had already organized the Central Pacific Railroad; later they completed the western part of the first transcontinental railroad, and Stanford himself drove the golden spike. They also bought out the San Francisco and San Jose Railroad, which had reached Mayfield (now Palo Alto's California Avenue district) in 1863 and San Jose early the next year.

In 1874, Stanford, who presided over the Central Pacific (later the Southern Pacific), moved from Sacramento to a Nob Hill mansion in San Francisco. A fancier of trotters and racehorses, he sought a country retreat. He found one near *el Palo Alto*, the landmark redwood where the first exploring Spaniards had camped in 1769. There the governor built up a horse farm that became America's most famous. Gradually he acquired more than 8,000 acres.

1890			1891	1892	1893	1894
Sherman Anti-trust Act begins federal effort to curb monopolies.	New York conducts first execution by electrocution.	Battle of Wounded Knee: Last major clash with Indians.	London is world capital of finance, shipping and insurance.	Ellis Island opens as immigration depot in New York.	Financial panic begins 4-year depression.	First showing of Edison's kineto-scope (motion pictures).

Stanford and his wife, Jane Lathrop Stanford, were touring Europe when their only son, Leland Jr., 15, contracted typhoid fever and died in Italy in 1884. The heartbroken parents soon decided that his memorial would be a university, with their Palo Alto estate part of its unprecedented $20 million endowment. Plans for the project dominated Stanford's attention, even after the California Legislature elected him a United States senator. In business he

Stanford University (circa 1898)

had met many eastern college graduates whose education had left them ill-prepared for the workaday world. One of the standards he set was that the university qualify its students for "personal success and direct usefulness in life." David Starr Jordan, chosen as the founding president, fully respected this wish as well as Stanford's insistence that the sciences be given their proper place, not denied it as on most other campuses of that era.

On October 1, 1891, Leland Stanford Junior University opened. Enrollment at the tuition-free institution almost doubled expectations—440, about one-quarter women. By the second semester it had swelled to 559, many more than were then enrolled at the University of California at Berkeley. The professed wish of the grieving Stanfords that "The children of California shall be our children" had begun to be fulfilled. And from its start, the university served not just the children of California but of the world.

Pioneer professors welcomed the practicality Senator Stanford preached and President Jordan championed. Particularly in the sciences and engineering, they set a tradition of intensive field work, as well as classroom lectures, laboratory experiments and book study. Both as consultants and as teachers, they made league with leaders of industry, business, and government in their fields so their students would understand what needed to be done in the "real world."

Herbert C. Hoover arrived in Palo Alto early for tutoring before he joined the pioneer Class of 1895; he can be called the university's first student. His rapid rise to the top ranks of mining engineers offered one example of Stanford's success in educating students for useful lives. About two decades later Hoover organized World War I food relief, then served as a Cabinet officer and President of the United States.

Palo Alto, a town laid out by Timothy Hopkins with the help of a loan cosigned by Leland Stanford, grew quickly, although the land had been left in hayfields until 1890. Its residents voted to incorporate in 1894. From the start, Stanford professors played key roles in the town's civic affairs. Engineering professors Charles D. (Daddy) Marx and Charles B. Wing were leaders in gaining city ownership of all major utilities—a rarity, and the base for a strong infrastructure when high technology came to town in the 1950s.

Before the turn of the century, electrical engineering Professor Frederic A.C. Perrine teamed up with students to field-test a locally developed high-potential oil switch. It made possible construction of 40,000-volt lines across the state, harnessing water power in a locale far from coal sources. In 1905, Professor Harris J. (Paddy) Ryan, a transmission research pioneer at Cornell University, came west to head the Stanford electrical engineering faculty. He too promoted university-industry cooperation, as did another man who joined the faculty in 1904, William F. Durand, the leading authority on airplane propeller design.

Senator Stanford's death in June 1893 plunged the university into a money crisis. While lawsuits tied up his estate, Mrs. Stanford devoted intense effort, personal income, and even her jewels to seeing that the university survived. The estate won in court. Under the founding grant, Mrs. Stanford controlled the endowment until 1902, when she empowered the Board of Trustees. A new round of campus construction was almost completed when she died in 1905.

At that point, Stanford did not rank among the world's foremost universities. But its foundations were well laid. Its blending of the ideals of excellence, practicality, and success bore a portent of revolutionary advances.

1895
Marconi experiments in wireless telegraphy.

Röntgen first to demonstrate the X-ray.

1896
Democrats nominate Bryan after "Cross of Gold" speech.

1898
Battleship Maine blows up at Havana.

U.S. annexes republic of Hawaii.

Marie and Pierre Curie discover radium.

1901
McKinley assassinated by anarchist's bullets.

In true Silicon Valley fashion, Abbott was established to fill a need—and in its founder's home. This start-up, however, made its debut not in this century or even in the last.

Abbott—then known as the Abbott Alkaloidal Company—began innovating new health care technologies in 1888, and has been serving that mission ever since. Its continuous growth and its focus on breakthrough technology has made Abbott a major player among the valley's health care innovators.

The man behind the company was Wallace Calvin Abbott, the son of a Vermont farmer who started his career as a doctor outside Chicago. Unhappy with the then-current ways to fight disease, Dr. Abbott began to manufacture granules of active, or alkaloidal, substances to better treat his patients. By doing so he became one of the early leaders of the modern scientific practice of pharmacy.

Abbott's headquarters are located in Abbott Park, Ill.

Since those pioneering days, Abbott has championed scientific investigation to benefit people everywhere and has devoted itself to discovering new medicines, new technologies, and new ways to manage health. The company's products now include a broad range of pharmaceuticals, diagnostics, medical devices, and nutritional products. Abbott's pharmaceuticals include the HIV treatment Kaletra®; HUMIRA®, a monoclonal antibody therapy for multiple autoimmune diseases; and the cholesterol-fighting drugs TriCor® and Niaspan®. Its nutritional products include the infant formula Similac® and the food supplement for people with diabetes, Glucerna®. Abbott's key medical products include the ARCHITECT®, PRISM®, and m2000™ diagnostic instrument systems; the FreeStyle® family of glucose monitoring products; and the XIENCE™ V Everolimus Eluting Coronary Stent System, which was designed in the Valley, is currently available in Europe and Asia Pacific, and is an investigational device in the United States and Japan.

Abbott has a long history of scientific advances that have improved the health of people around the world. In the 1920s and 1930s, Abbott made important breakthroughs in the collection and storage of blood and blood products and intravenous solutions, making transfusions safer and more reliable for patients. In later years, the company introduced high-volume hematology instruments used in hospital labs and blood banks. Abbott's PRISM system, a high-throughput analyzer, is currently used to screen the majority of the world's blood supply.

Abbott is also a proven leader in sedation and anesthesia. Dr. Ernest Volwiler and later, Dr. Donalee Tabern, conducted pioneering work that led to the introduction of the sedatives Neonal and Nembutal.

Building on their previous work, in 1936 Drs. Volwiler and Tabern developed Pentothal, an intravenous anesthetic that enabled doctors to develop many of the more complex surgical procedures that define modern medicine today. For their efforts, Drs. Volwiler and Tabern were inducted into the National Inventors Hall of Fame 50 years later, in 1986.

Some of Abbott's most significant scientific contributions are in the area of HIV/AIDS. In 1985, the company developed the first licensed test to detect HIV antibodies in the blood and today

Abbott's founder, Dr. Wallace C. Abbott, was one of the leaders in the practice of modern pharmacy.

Dr. Ernest Volwiler, a member of the National Inventors Hall of Fame, pictured in his lab, was one of the inventors of Pentothal, a widely used anesthetic.

remains a leader in HIV diagnostics. Abbott researchers continue to monitor HIV-positive populations for new strains and resistance in order to refine its diagnostics.

Abbott scientists also developed two protease inhibitors for the treatment of HIV, Norvir (one of the first introduced) and Kaletra (the most prescribed). The protease inhibitor class of drugs has revolutionized HIV treatment, helping turn HIV/AIDS into a manageable disease.

Silicon Valley today is home to many biotechnology companies, but Abbott can trace its biotech roots back to the early 1900s, with the production of Abbott's book *Biologic Products and How to Use Them*. Since then, Abbott has continued to be at the leading edge of biologics research and development.

Abbott's introduction of a new method for penicillin production in the 1940s ultimately allowed the critical antibiotic to be produced on a scale large enough to supply the U.S. war effort. In 1972, the company introduced one of the first antibody-based tests for hepatitis and continued to contribute new, more sensitive tests in the years that followed. In addition to the first HIV test, Abbott has delivered additional retroviral and hepatitis tests, which are used to screen more than half of the world's donated blood supply.

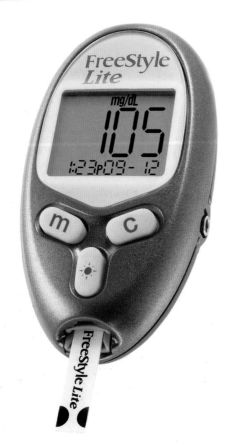

Alameda-based Abbott Diabetes Care markets the FreeStyle® family of blood glucose monitors.

In the 1990s, Abbott began molecular diagnostics research, introducing a DNA-based system for infectious diseases. Since then, the company has developed gene-based tests for breast and bladder cancer.

In 2002, Abbott received U.S. Food and Drug Administration approval for its innovative biologic, HUMIRA, the first fully human monoclonal antibody for rheumatoid arthritis (RA). HUMIRA treats several autoimmune diseases including RA, psoriatic arthritis, ankylosing spondylitis (arthritis of the spine), and Crohn's disease, and is in development for psoriasis and ulcerative colitis use.

Abbott also has worked with other biotechnology companies. Abbott was a key early investor in Amgen, the world's largest biotech company. In 2007, biotechnology company Genentech recognized the potential of two Abbott-discovered cancer compounds and partnered with Abbott to develop and commercialize them.

Abbott's investigational XIENCE™ V drug eluting stent, developed by Abbott Vascular in Santa Clara, is based upon the world's most popular bare metallic stent platform, the MULTI-LINK VISION®. Stents are tiny mesh tubes used to prop open clogged arteries.

As the company grew globally, so did Abbott's presence in Silicon Valley. In the 1970s, Abbott established a site in Santa Clara for the diagnostics division. In 1986, Abbott acquired the Mountain View-based company Oximetrix. In Mountain View, Abbott employees manufactured drug-delivery pumps for hospitals, including the first morphine-delivery pump. This division moved to Morgan Hill in 1997 and later became part of the Abbott spin-off, Hospira.

Abbott Vascular, a leader in vascular care technologies, has locations in both Redwood City and Santa Clara. Abbott Diabetes Care, based in Alameda, is a leader in developing, manufacturing, and marketing advanced glucose-monitoring systems and test strips for better diabetes management. In all, Abbott employs over 2,500 professionals in Silicon Valley.

With more than $22 billion in 2006 sales, Abbott's 65,000 employees work to address critical needs across the health care

Abbott and its philanthropic foundation, Abbott Fund, have helped hundreds of thousands of children and families in the developing world who are impacted by HIV/AIDS.

spectrum. Miles White, chairman of the board and CEO, states that the company's success "is a function and reflection of the people who make it work." Abbott's success is also due to the fact that it is a committed global citizen. "Global citizenship is simply inseparable from our mission of improving lives," says Mr. White. To that end, Abbott focuses on advancing leading-edge science and technologies, educating patients, increasing access and affordability to its medicines and technologies, advancing health-related public policy dialogue, and working to improve the environment through initiatives that include cutting greenhouse gas emissions and water consumption.

Throughout its history, Abbott has maintained a commitment to the people it serves—patients, medical professionals, and employees—around the world and in Silicon Valley.

Miles D. White has served as Abbott's chairman of the board and chief executive officer since 1999.

Getting the Money to Start

"When we raised the venture capital for Adobe, we had a very different business plan than the one that we eventually executed and I've often remarked, "Thank God we did not pursue that plan because we probably would not have survived."

— **Charles Geschke**
Founder, Adobe Systems

"I funded Atari with $250 and grew it, not because I thought that was a nifty way to start a company, but because venture capital was not available to me. I mean, it may sound ludicrous at this point in time, but people thought the idea of playing games on a television set was the stupidest idea they'd ever heard of."

— **Nolan Bushnell**
Founder, Atari

"We talked to over 25 venture capital firms. And no one wanted to fund us. And no venture capital firm did."

— **Scott Cook**
Founder, Intuit

"In 1980, 1981 and even up to 1983, there was a great deal of increase in venture capital funding, and Lam Research was born at that time — and we were funded a hundred percent by venture capitalists."

— **David K. Lam**
Founder, Lam Research

"When we went and talked to venture capitalists and none of them would give us any money, one of them referred to me as a "renegade from the human race" because I had longer hair then. And you know, none of them would give us any money. Thank God! Because then they would have ended up owning most of our company. So, I think that Apple and a few other companies were good examples to the venture capitalists that great ideas are not the exclusive providence of people with gray hair."

— **Steve Jobs**
Founder, Apple Computer

"For 15 million dollars we were going to get 30 percent of the company and we went home that night and said, "You know we really don't need 15 million dollars to get this thing started. All we need is five." So we went back to the venture capital people the next day and said, "Listen, can we have 70 percent of the company if we only get 5 million?" And they laughed and said, "Okay, fine. Okay, we'll do that."

— **Robert Swanson**
Founder, Linear Technologies

Arc Converter at Federal Telegraph

Communication by wire had come to the Peninsula in 1853, when California State Telegraph lines were strung from San Francisco to San Jose, then east to Stockton, Sacramento and Marysville. Completion of the San Francisco-San Jose rail line a decade later added stations and Morse Code operators at depots.

Alexander Graham Bell's invention of the telephone in 1876 rang a San Jose harmonic in 1880 when the Sunset Telephone Company was organized there. Telephone service grew slowly until almost the turn of the century, then spurted.

Wireless telephony was in the wind as Stanford University opened in 1891. In 1888, Heinrich Hertz had demonstrated that James Clerk Maxwell's predictions concerning electromagnetic waves were correct, at least for short distances. The press reported Hertz's experiments and those of Guglielmo Marconi, an Italian physicist working in England, who in 1898 broadcast a Morse Code signal across the English Channel. Reading of this and witnessing experiments by his Stanford physics professor, a science-minded student from San Jose named Charles David Herrold repeated Marconi's tests in his home laboratory. He managed to send signals over a distance of one mile.

A few years later, the *San Francisco Call* used wireless to flash the news that a troop ship bringing American soldiers home from Manila was near the Golden Gate. Soon military networks were being linked up.

When Marconi sent a dot-dot-dot signal (the Morse letter S) across the Atlantic in 1901, his feat was widely reported. At Stanford, it stirred keen interest among the professors — and their sons. "Wireless" experiments required no complex equipment — a cylindrical Quaker Oats box wound with copper wire, a crystal and a "cat's whisker" wire were about all it took to tune in.

Meanwhile, inventors were aiming to improve Marconi's transmitting system. In San Francisco, Francis McCarty, 17, son of Leland Stanford's head coachman, began to develop a promising damped-wave method. But in the aftermath of the 1906 earthquake, the youth was killed by a runaway horse. Two investors, the Henshaw brothers of Oakland, asked Professor Ryan at Stanford to name someone to continue McCarty's work. Ryan turned to Cyril Elwell, a recent engineering graduate who had succeeded in developing electric smelting techniques.

Elwell set up shop in Palo Alto, where radio had gained a toehold. Douglas Perham had built the first radio spark transmitter in town in 1906, and later moved it to his house and machine shop at 913 Emerson Street. Three amateurs were active locally: James Arthur Miller, who in 1907 had built a 75-foot antenna mast and set up the first radio station in town, and two professor's sons, Daddy Marx's boy Roland and George Branner. Elwell bought a house at 1451 Cowper Street and put up two 75-foot wooden masts. Turning the bungalow into a wireless telephone station, he broadcast a wavering version of "The Blue Danube" to stations about five miles away in Los Altos and Mountain View.

After testing the McCarty system for a year, Elwell concluded that it was inadequate — only continuous waves (C.W.) would serve the need he saw for reliable commercial wireless transmissions that could compete with

Cyril Elwell

1903
Wilbur and Orville Wright complete first powered flight.

1905
Defeat by Japan checks Russia's Asian expansionism.

1907
Albert Einstein states his Theory of Relativity.

16 battleships of U.S. "Great White Fleet" cruise around the world.

Steamship Lusitania crosses Atlantic in 5 days.

1908
Henry Ford produces the first Model T automobile; price: $850.

- 20 -

Federal Telegraph's Palo Alto Switches

cable companies for lucrative traffic. Knowing Danish scientist Valdemar Poulsen had produced C.W. with an arc converter, Elwell telegraphed Poulsen asking how much he wanted for U.S. rights. The price proved too steep; the Henshaws withdrew from the project and Elwell bought their equipment for $250. Then he sailed to Denmark and made a deal with Poulsen. Returning with a small arc converter he bought, Elwell failed to elicit backing in New York, where promoters of Marconi's system and others had given wireless a bad reputation. Back in Palo Alto, Stanford President Jordan offered to invest $500, and with that as a cachet, Elwell enrolled other faculty members — particularly Professor Marx — as investors in the Poulsen Wireless Telephone and Telegraph Company, founded in 1909.

Elwell bought Perham's house and shop in 1910. It served as the apparatus factory for what, in 1911, became Federal Telegraph Company. The company demonstrated 50-mile, two-way C.W. communication between Sacramento and Stockton. Next came a 2,100-mile transmission to Honolulu, using 300-foot masts designed by Professor Wing. Then the company built a U.S. network of 16 high-power wireless stations, and in 1912 opened a San Francisco-Hawaii commercial wireless route.

The arcs enabled Federal to focus signals in a narrow band, unlike the older systems, but they needed continuous improvement. Lee de Forest, who in 1906 had invented a three-element vacuum tube he called the audion, asked for a job in 1911 and Elwell made him research director. Technician Charles Logwood and telephone engineer Herbert Van Etten were added to form a radio research team. Besides improving C.W. and the arcs, the trio experimented with de Forest's audions, which had only been applied as a wireless signal detector. Cascading a series of tubes, they developed the first genuine amplifier, showing how it could make a fly's steps on a sheet of paper sound like an army's marching boots, and airing voices 2 1/2 blocks from the lab.

The team also noted "squeals and howls" in a repeater circuit — signs of feedback that could create a self-regenerating oscillation. Decades later the U.S. Supreme Court awarded the feedback invention patent to de Forest, based on the lab notes. The audion, after improvement in the East, became the key component of all radio, telephone, radar, television, and computer systems until the invention of the transistor in 1947.

About the time Elwell was airing "The Blue Danube" in 1909, Charles D. Herrold, by 1909 nicknamed "Doc" because he headed a college in San Jose for training engineers and telegraphers, broadcast voice and music from "San Jose Calling," a station he first identified as FN. Herrold used an arc transmitter of his own design. In 1912 Herrold began regularly scheduled broadcasts — apparently America's first. His station later became KQW and then KCBS. Among his listeners in 1914 was a Stanford faculty member's son, Fred Terman, who with future U.S. president Herbert Hoover Jr. had built a spark set.

Lee de Forest

1909
Adm. Robert Peary reaches North Pole on 6th try.

French aviator Louis Bierot makes first airplane flight across the English Channel.

Newsreels become part of popular movie fare.

1910
The Union of South Africa is formed.

1911
Norwegian explorer Roald Amundsen reaches the South Pole.

1912
British ocean liner Titanic sinks off Newfoundland.

First O.C. McDonald store front

The retro "Oh See!" neon sign that points the way to O. C. McDonald's San Jose, California, site reflects the fact that this installer of plumbing, process piping, heating, ventilation, and air conditioning is hometown grown and was founded in another era. The fact that its client list now includes such high-tech giants as Intel and Applied Materials and that the company is focused on providing solutions to all the industries in Santa Clara Valley, with its own cleanroom for prefabricating clean piping systems and plumbing and sheet metal fabrication facilities, shows that it's also a state-of-the-art industry leader of the 21st century.

Change and determination are at the heart of O. C. McDonald's long history and success. In 1906, Oren Charles (O. C.) McDonald, company founder and great-grandfather of current president Jim McDonald, turned to plumbing and fixing wells to supplement the income from his Milpitas chicken ranch. Shortly after, he found that the plumbing business was more lucrative than the chickens, and consequently O. C. McDonald Plumbing opened its doors in San Jose.

When Oren's son E.V. (Vic) later took over the business, he widened its reach by moving the company into industrial/defense projects, including building metal U.S. Navy lifeboats during World War II, and projects for the Food Machinery Corporation. He also installed in the late 1940s the first air-conditioning systems in what would later be Silicon Valley, and moved the company to its present location, on W. San Carlos Street in San Jose.

As great changes occurred in the valley during the 1960s through 1980s, more changes occurred at O. C. McDonald. The founder's grandson, R. V. (Dick) McDonald, took over leadership, introducing two-way radios to the company's service trucks, the first company in the area to have them, and computers to the office. Dick also took on such challenging projects as the Ford and General Motors assembly plants, the San Jose/Santa Clara Waste Water Treatment Plant, and O'Connor and Good Samaritan Hospitals.

Today, current president Jim McDonald, who started in the family business sweeping floors and driving trucks, continues his predecessors' drive to service and grow along with the ever-changing Silicon Valley. Under his leadership, the company has been modernized and now specializes in high-tech cleanroom construction as well as process tool installations and heavy indus-trial piping. Recent notable projects include the NASA Unitary Wind Tunnel, Intel, the Stanford Linear Accelerator, Applied Materials, Spanish Bay Hotel, the Metcalf Energy Center, and

Marriott Hotel construction in San Jose, California.

the San Jose Biotech Incubator. The bio-pharmaceutical industry may be the next growth area for the business.

Despite the company's forward-looking approach—it's good to learn from the past, Jim McDonald says, but he always looks to the future—O. C. McDonald has never lost its focus on providing old-fashioned service and expert workmanship. "We are known for quality and timely installation," McDonald states, "and do our best to deliver what the customer needs. No job is too big or too small."

Today, O. C. McDonald, which employs more than 200 professionals, is also known for being involved in the Silicon Valley community. "We're a local company and I want people to know that," says McDonald. The company has been active in the Chamber of Commerce for more than 75 years and in Rotary for three generations, and generously supports local charitable organizations.

Process tool installation in Class 1 Cleanroom, Milpitas, California.

Chapter 4: An Industry Rises—Federal Telegraph

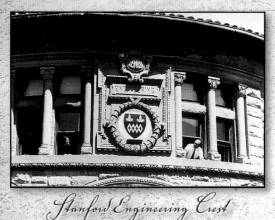

Stanford Engineering Crest

As 1913 dawned, Federal Telegraph Company was off to a great start. It had the best technology of the day, a capable chief engineer in Cyril Elwell, and an outstanding research team led by Lee de Forest. And it was able to hire the cream of Stanford's electrical engineering graduates. But the company was due to experience problems that became common in Silicon Valley later on—defections, spinoffs and money troubles. Even so, it was upward bound.

De Forest soon left to sell his audion improvements, to which Federal had only "shop rights." They were bought by American Telephone and Telegraph, whose engineers had been unable to develop repeaters to boost long-distance calls beyond 900 miles. Elwell, meanwhile, had lost financial control of the firm to promoters whose manipulations embarrassed him and Professor Wing as directors representing the Stanford investors. He joined a British company in 1913.

Besides the research team disbanding, Federal lost two Danes who had come over to install the Stockton-Sacramento circuit, engineer Peter V. Jensen and mechanic C. Albertus, as well as the first American electrical engineer Elwell had hired, E.S. Pridham, a talented Stanford graduate. The three quit to develop a loudspeaker, and the moving-coil principle they used in work at Napa and Oakland led to formation of a successful company, Magnavox. Such speakers were to be used at public assemblages and in millions of radio receivers.

Federal still had plenty of talent. Leonard Fuller, a Cornell graduate with wide-ranging experience, and Harold Elliott took the lead as Federal began developing U.S. Navy communications. Roland Marx helped perfect the giant arcs. Elliott later developed a radio broadcast receiver for mass production, and many radio pushbutton tuning devices. After the United States entered World War I in 1917, Federal ballooned to 300 employees, housed in a plant on El Camino Real south of University Avenue. Near the end of the war Federal built a giant station near Bordeaux, France, with James Arthur Miller the principal engineer. Its arcs were workhorses at all major American naval bases.

Audion Detector

During the war, the government ordered the few widely scattered civilian broadcasters, including Doc Herrold, to shut down. Herrold turned to training military operators.

After Armistice Day in 1918, a new technological era began. Arc transmitters were being outmoded by improved tubes. Herrold, for one, had to junk the broadcast equipment he had invented and replace it at an exacting cost.

Although government work slacked off as peace settled in, radio was due for great expansion. Federal carried on its long lines and shore-to-ship traffic, and also developed new products. Frederick Kolster, who had invented the radio direction-finder in 1913, worked as Federal's chief research engineer from 1921 to 1931. Kolster produced a radio compass and radio receivers and did experiments with big parabolic directional antennas.

In 1921, Federal built a transmitting station in the Palo Alto baylands, employing a 626-foot mast designed with the help of Professor Wing. The Marsh

Lee de Forest, center, at 1915 exposition

1912	**1915**	**1917**		**1919**	**1920**
Ottoman Empire loses almost all lands in Europe.	German Zeppelin airships bomb Britain in first airship raids; (1915-16).	Russian Revolution and the abdication of the tsar.	Lenin's bolsheviks take power.	Earnest Rutherford, English scientist, splits the atom.	Amendment to the U.S. constitution prohibits the sale of alcohol in the U.S.

Federal Telegraph's Station Near Bordeaux

Station was known by the radio call letters KWT (later KFS). Mackay Radio and Telegraph Company, soon to become a unit of International Telephone and Telegraph Company, bought the station in 1927 to use for point-to-point and ship-to-shore communications.

The Marsh Station switched from arcs to more efficient vacuum-tube oscillators in 1935—a conversion marking the start of shortwave radio. The mast stood until 1960. Federal's transition from arcs to tubes spanned the years 1927 to 1934. A key figure in that era was engineer Charles V. Litton, a Stanford graduate who became fascinated by tube-blowing as a teenager.

In 1931 Federal Telegraph's manufacturing operations were moved to New Jersey after company officials decided Palo Alto was too far away from sources of supplies, skilled labor, and key markets. ITT eventually swallowed the company. Among the Federal employees who decided not to go East was Charlie Litton. Instead, he started his own company in Redwood City, where his tube-developing skill was a boon to remaining Peninsula radio operations. Another who stayed behind, Gerhard R. Fisher, developed the M-scope, a detector of metal and water as deep as 20 feet underground.

Frederick Emmons Terman, the son of famed Stanford psychologist Lewis Terman, also worked at Federal Telegraph briefly in the course of taking chemistry and electrical engineering degrees at Stanford. Then Terman went on to the Massachusetts Institute of Technology to earn a Ph.D. under Vannevar Bush. Terman was slated to teach at MIT, but while home at Stanford for the summer came down with tuberculosis. In 1927 Harris J. Ryan offered Terman a half-time position at Stanford teaching radio engineering courses. After fully recovering, Terman stayed at Stanford to run a new lab. Before long he had written the leading textbook on radio engineering, an earlier name for electronics.

A few other facts about the 1912-32 era foreshadowed later epochs. Brothers Russell and Sigurd Varian, Palo Altans as boys, had moved to Halcyon, south of San Luis Obispo. To enroll at Stanford to study physics, Russell Varian walked the 200 miles to the campus. Meanwhile, another professor's son who spent his boyhood in Palo Alto from 1913 to 1922 was a science-struck fellow named William Shockley.

The year 1931 brought another development that was destined to take the area into outer space: Bay Area people raised more than $476,000 to purchase and sell for $1 to the U.S. government the land for what became Moffett Field, initially a naval air station for dirigibles.

Despite the Depression and Federal's departure, there was light at the end of the tunnel.

Dirigible over Moffet Naval Air Station

1922
Tutankhamen's tomb is discovered.

1923
Dr. F.G. Banting discovers insulin, treatment for diabetes.

1927
Lindbergh completes the first nonstop solo flight from N.Y. to Paris.

1928
Alexander Fleming discovers penicillin, the first antibiotic.

1929
Wall Street crash leads to the Great Depression; 2300 U.S. banks fail.

1930
Gas turbine is invented.

When two young Stanford University graduates—George E. (Pat) Carey and Herbert J. Cornish—opened Cornish & Carey in 1935 in Palo Alto, two other companies were just opening. HP and Varian would become technology leaders, and Cornish & Carey would be inextricably linked with the high-tech boom that followed their founding.

By the time Cornish & Carey Commercial Chairman Scott Carey moved to Palo Alto as a young lawyer in 1962, Silicon Valley was, in his words, "All apricots and Stanford Indians" (now called the Stanford Cardinal). By 1969, when Carey joined the family firm as a commercial broker, apricots were giving way to concrete tilt-up buildings for research and development and "brilliant graduates from the Stanford school of engineering and its business school were starting new Silicon Valley companies like Cisco and Sun Microsystems."

Carey says that while the first high-tech companies were in the Stanford Industrial Park, new companies began to migrate south to Sunnyvale and Mountain View. C&C worked with them from their commercial office in Palo Alto and opened a second office in Sunnyvale. Not sure that this migration south was going to last, the "office" was a trailer. "We couldn't find a garage," Carey said.

"We worked with tenants to figure out not only what they needed then but what they might need later. For example, we put Silicon Graphics into their first 5,000-square-foot space in Mountain View and stayed with them until they eventually grew into 1 million square feet. We grew with them, and that happened with a lot of our clients." As companies spilled over into communities all over northern California, Cornish & Carey, Carey says, "went with them,

George E. Carey

Palo Alto, California

opening offices in San Mateo, Sacramento, and the East Bay." Today Cornish & Carey Commercial has a staff of 272 people, including a consulting group, and nine strategically located northern California offices.

Under Chuck Seufferlein, President and CEO, Cornish & Carey Commercial has added services as customers need them. The Client Solutions team offers consulting on strategic planning and financial advice. C&C Capital provides mortgage placement and debt financing. C&C also developed specialist groups to meet the needs of the ancillary markets that grew up with the "boom" industries.

Cornish & Carey forged a relationship with ONCOR International to service global commercial real estate needs with a comprehensive selection of corporate and investor services in more than 200 markets throughout the world. In 2006, C&C leased over 22,858,086 square feet, sold more than 13,708,134 square feet, and closed some 2,695 transactions.

Carey now sees a bright future for biotech, as well as innovative conservation and alternative energy technologies. According to Carey, Silicon Valley will lead these new industries because, "There's a certain synergy and critical mass here that's hard to duplicate and that creates its own energy. It's not going to go away. The future is going to be just as exciting."

Cornish & Carey Commercial plans to be here too, with the knowledge and the ability to think along with clients about what they need today and tomorrow, and the expertise to provide solutions.

Chapter 5: The Great Depression—Back to the Lab

Philo Farnsworth

The Depression held the United States in a paralyzing grip, crimping industrial operations and pinching funding for costly academic research. It was a time to learn, apply brainpower, and make do in the laboratory at minimal cost.

Federal Telegraph's move East had closed the Palo Alto-Stanford area's major production plant, but it left behind some engineers and skilled workers who chose to stay in the West. At the university, Fred Terman was firmly entrenched as the leading U.S. academic man in radio engineering. Even before becoming Electrical Engineering department head in 1937, Terman encouraged his students to start businesses. He took them to San Francisco to visit places like Heintz & Kaufman's radio plant and Philo Farnsworth's television development workshop.

John Kaar began developing mobile radio communication from his Menlo Park garage, later moving Kaar Engineering to Palo Alto. First he equipped the dog-catcher with a mobile radio. Then, with Terman's advice, Kaar installed a police-fire network linking Palo Alto and nearby towns. Messages went from base to vehicles in the field at first, but soon became two-way.

Leonard Fuller, Federal's ex-chief, headed electrical engineering at the University of California. He arranged for Federal to give Berkeley a leftover 80-ton, 1000-kilowatt arc generator. With it, atom-smashing pioneer Ernest O. Lawrence built his first successful cyclotron.

In 1934, Eitel-McCullough began fabricating vacuum tubes in San Carlos, enlarging a Bay Area tube production cluster dating back to 1916-20. Charles V. Litton, another ex-Federal star, set up Litton Electronics in Redwood City to produce custom vacuum tubes and tube-making machinery. Litton patented some multigrid tubes in which oscillations occurred and assigned the patents to Stanford.

At Physics Corner on campus, William W. Hansen, Russell Varian's former roommate, was new on the faculty. Hansen hankered to do nuclear research, but the money shortage kept him from using X-ray tubes and the Ryan High Voltage Laboratory. Using resonance techniques instead, he developed a cavity resonator to accelerate electrons. The copper container could be made to act as an excellent radio-frequency circuit, capable of developing extremely high voltages with modest power input. He called it a *rumbatron*.

Rus Varian, meanwhile, had worked for a time as a chemist assisting Philo Farnsworth, and then in the East. His younger brother, Sigurd, a former Pan American World Airways pilot in Latin America, persuaded Rus to

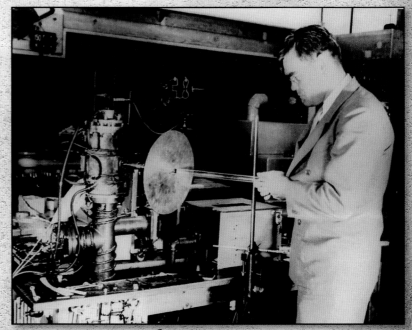

William Hansen

1933
Adolf Hitler, chancellor and virtual dictator, leads extreme national Nazi party in Germany. Hitler establishes a totalitarian state and uses millions of Jews for slave labor in concentration camps where they suffered starvation, torture, and ultimately death.

1934
Mao Zedong and Zhu De lead communists on Long March through China hoping to find sanctuary.

1935
W.H. Carothers invents polyamide fibers (including nylon in 1937).

Daredevil Sig Varian's Plane...

...after crash

come home to Halcyon and set up a lab. Sig envisioned an aircraft navigation and detection system to save pilots' lives in darkness or storms. Hearing about Hansen's rumbatron, Rus Varian wrote him to say it might fit their needs. So a collaboration began that brought the Varians to Stanford. They got physics lab space plus $100 a year for materials in exchange for half of any eventual patent earnings.

In their collaboration, Rus Varian generated ideas, Bill Hansen sifted out the promising ones, and Sig Varian built prototypes. By mid-1937, Russell had proposed a way to make the rumbatron an oscillator or amplifier that modulated streams of electrons into powerful waves. Sigurd sought such pulses of high-frequency energy to bounce off aircraft, ships, or ground features—the principle of radar. Soon they had a new electron tube. They named it the klystron.

The invention excited the Sperry Gyroscope Company of New York. Sperry licensed the klystron patents and, for an extra $1,000, the patent rights Charles Litton had given Stanford. Litton insisted that the money go to the engineering school for research on electronic tubes. Fred Terman allocated it to graduate student support, specifically for David Packard, one of "Terman's boys" who had been working on vacuum tubes at General Electric in Schenectady, N.Y.

Packard and a radio lab buddy, William R. Hewlett, encouraged by Terman, had talked about starting a company after graduating in 1934, but GE's offer of a job took Packard East. After completing graduate work at MIT, Hewlett returned to Stanford and continued his research in the radio lab. By mid-1938, Packard was back in Palo Alto with the intent of "making a run for it" in business with Hewlett. In a small garage behind the flat Dave and Lucile Packard rented at 367 Addison Avenue, the two friends began to explore product ideas, including one for a continuously variable broadcast turning condenser suggested by Terman. It was here they perfected their idea of an improved audio oscillator, the HP Model 200A—the basis for the partnership they established formally on January 1, 1939.

When the chief sound engineer for Walt Disney Studios got wind of the 200A, it was through his interest and request for modifications that Disney Studios placed Hewlett-Packard's first big order—for eight "Model 200B" audio oscillators for sound production of the movie *Fantasia*. The oscillators were modestly priced at $71.50 each.

Another propitious event of the era was a decision by the National Advisory Committee on Aeronautics to set up NACA's second field laboratory on the West Coast. At Ames Research Center adjoining Moffett Field, ground was broken late in 1939. Its initial research facilities, including several wind tunnels, were dedicated in the spring of 1940.

At Stanford, meanwhile, the klystron stepped up microwave research. Terman directed Edward Ginzton and other electrical engineering graduate students to assist Hansen in klystron improvement, for which Sperry had given Stanford $10,000. Before relocating with his physics team to Sperry's Long Island facility, Hansen taught a special class on the klystron for Terman's graduate students, creating a new generation of trained microwave engineers and preparing them for war work.

1935
Amelia Earhart leaves Honolulu on first solo flight across the Pacific.

Stalin sends millions to harsh prison labor camps.

1936
Civil War in Spain; (1936-39).

1937
Italy, Germany, and Japan form an anticommunist pact.

1939
German troops invade Poland. World War II begins; (1939-45).

The first jet aircraft flies.

On New Year's Day in 1939, David Packard and William R. Hewlett tossed a coin in a rented Palo Alto garage to decide the order of names for their new company. They had started their business months earlier, with $538 and a few product ideas. In 2007, Hewlett-Packard Company has 156,000 employees doing business in more than 170 countries and the company's offerings span printing, personal computing, software, services and IT infrastructure, with revenues totaling $ 97 billion.

When Packard and Hewlett, who were classmates in Frederick E. Terman's radio engineering program at Stanford University, neared graduation, it was 1934 and the Depression gripped America. As Packard told it, "Bill and I had said if we can't get a job ourselves we'll just start our own company.... Fred encouraged us to do that."

Before HP started, however, Packard accepted a position with General Electric in Schenectady, N.Y. Hewlett became a graduate student at Massachusetts Institute of Technology and then studied with Terman again at Stanford, where he developed a resistance-tuned oscillator. The two men's business start marked time until Terman drew Packard back to Stanford on a graduate fellowship. In 1938, Hewlett and Packard began part-time work in the garage behind Dave and Lucile Packard's ground floor flat at 367 Addison Avenue. Hewlett bunked in the backyard shed.

In 1939, David Packard (seated) and William R. Hewlett produced an innovative audio oscillator.

Before long, Walt Disney Studios placed an order for eight HP 200B audio oscillators for the movie *Fantasia*—HP's first big sale. By 1942, the company had built a plant in Palo Alto, though it was still a small operation when World War II, as Hewlett put it, "changed everything." The Army Signal Corps called Hewlett to duty; Packard ran HP as it moved into war work, making audio oscillators used in proximity fuzes and microwave-signal generators used in radar and counter-radar measures.

An incentive plan allowing employees to share in earnings enabled HP to keep a strong work force despite wartime wage controls; later it became the basis for a profit-sharing plan widely emulated throughout Silicon Valley and beyond. Other "people-centered" practices followed as the founders fostered a work environment that aimed for innovation and achievement, promoted trust in people and teamwork, and rewarded employees for HP's success.

When Bill Hewlett (left) returned from WWII Army duty, he and Dave Packard put HP into microwave measurement.

In 1947, the year HP incorporated, revenues topped $1.5 million. Three years later, when the Korean conflict began and electronics production soared, the company had in place an expanded line of test equipment, including microwave and high-frequency products. In 1957, HP had its first public stock offering and began manufacturing at its new flagship site in Stanford Research Park, home of HP's current corporate offices.

Soon HP grew its product offerings through a series of acquisitions, all within its focused field of interest—electronics manufacturing. HP pursued new opportunities in data printing, medical electronics, and analytical instrumentation in the United States and entered international markets in 1959 with marketing operations in Geneva, Switzerland and a manufacturing plant in Böblingen, Germany. In 1966, HP Laboratories—today among the world's premier technology labs—was formed as the company's central research facility. HP's first computer, designed as a controller for test and measurement instruments, was also introduced in 1966.

In 1970, recession hit. Rather than reduce its work force, HP instituted a temporary 10% hours-and-pay reduction. Everyone contributed to the necessary cost savings, and six months later, everyone returned to a full work week. Despite adverse economic trends, HP continued to develop new technologies and products, tightening its belt rather than incurring long-term debt.

The slide rule, once the tool of every engineer, slipped into obsolescence after HP introduced the first scientific handheld calculator, the HP-35, in 1972. Also in 1972, the company ventured into business computing with the HP 3000 minicomputer.

In 1973, HP became the first company in the U.S. to institute another people-centric policy borrowed from HP GmbH in Germany: flextime. The practice of offering employees flexible working hours had met with great success in Europe and the decision was made to transplant it to HP sites in the U.S. It did not take long for this fresh approach to time management to spread throughout the technology sector.

The first scientific handheld calculator, introduced by HP in 1972, quickly wooed engineers away from slide rules.

After sales passed $1 billion in 1976, the founders again showed their willingness to delegate responsibility. John Young became president in 1977 and chief executive officer in 1978, supported by three executive vice presidents. Hewlett and Packard remained on the board of directors.

Focusing on innovation and quality, HP stayed a steady, profitable course as it introduced its first personal computer for technical users in 1980. Yokogawa Hewlett-Packard of Tokyo, Japan, a joint venture formed in 1963, won the prestigious Deming Prize for quality in 1982.

The new management team had its hands full during the 1980s, a time of increasing global competition and rapid change. Young led HP's success in the computer business. He also ousted the "not-invented-here" syndrome, contending that HP need not do everything itself but could use supplier alliances while capitalizing on its key strengths.

In 1984, HP helped create a new market for fast, inexpensive printing with the debut of the ThinkJet printer and the LaserJet printer, HP's most successful product ever. The next year, an epic R&D effort gave birth to an industry-leading family of Precision Architecture computer systems.

In 1987, Bill Hewlett retired as a director; Dave Packard relinquished his board chairmanship in 1993. Through separate family philanthropic foundations, both founders became significant benefactors of educational, scientific, and health-care institutions.

Dave Packard and Bill Hewlett (right) at the landmark dedication in 1989, their company's 50th anniversary year.

Lewis E. (Lew) Platt succeeded John Young as president and CEO in 1992. Platt, steeped in HP values, championed diversity in the workplace, a balance between work and personal life, and community involvement. By 1995, HP's product lines spanned a broad spectrum, including electronic test and measurement instruments and systems, networking products, medical electronic equipment, instruments and systems for chemical analysis, handheld calculators, and electronic components, as well as computer and computer-related products and services. By the mid-1990s, more than two-thirds of the company's revenues were generated abroad, principally in Europe. By then, HP manufacturing and research centers were widely dispersed in Europe, the Asia Pacific region, Latin America, Canada, and more than two dozen U.S. locations. More than 600 sales offices or independent distributorships served more than 120 countries.

During Platt's tenure, HP continued to be widely recognized for the company's culture, known as "The HP Way," once described by Bill Hewlett as "the policies and actions that flow from the belief that men and women want to do a good job, a creative job, and that if they are provided with the proper environment they will do so. Closely coupled with this is the HP tradition of treating each individual with consideration and respect, and recognizing individual achievements." Related values include uncompromising integrity, emphasis on teamwork to achieve common objectives and encouraging flexibility and innovation.

The Palo Alto garage where HP began. In 1989, it was designated California Landmark No. 976, "Birthplace of Silicon Valley."

In 1995, Dave Packard published *The HP Way: How Bill Hewlett and I Built Our Company*. The book chronicled the rise of HP, giving readers a firsthand look at the culture, business practices, and decentralized management style—management by objective and "management by walking around"—central to the company's sustained and remarkable success.

Under Platt's direction, the company's long track record of technical innovation continued, with emphasis on its expansion into computing through such corporate business systems as the HP 3000 and HP 9000 (1992). At the other end of the computing spectrum, the three-pound HP OmniBook 300, a laptop-sized "super-portable" computer (1993) boasted enough battery power to last during a flight across the continental U.S. In 1994 the company introduced its first color laser printer, the HP Color LaserJet, and shipped its 10 millionth LaserJet printer. In 1995 the introduction of the HP Pavilion PC marked the company's highly successful introduction into the home computer market, and in 1997 HP became one of the 30 stocks that comprised the Dow Jones Industrial Average.

HP's printer business continued its ascent with such new products as the OfficeJet printer-fax-copier, the company's first entry in the space-saving, all-in-one line. By 1995, environmental guidelines in product design, Energy Star certification, and a robust recycling program established the company as an industry leader in addressing issues of environmental responsibility. On the employee front, HP became one of the first companies to encourage telecommuting around the world (1994).

In 1996, the year of co-founder David Packard's death, HP revenue had risen to an astounding $38.4 billion annually and the company that made its first hire in 1939 employed 112,000 people worldwide.

The garage was comprehensively restored by HP in 2005.

At the pinnacle of the tech boom, in 1999, HP's board of directors announced the decision to spin off a new company in order to sharpen the strategic focus of HP's businesses. HP's former measurement, components, chemical and analysis and medical businesses became Agilent Technologies in Silicon Valley's largest IPO to date. HP retained its computing, printing and imaging businesses.

In July of 1999, Lew Platt retired. HP named Carleton (Carly) Fiorina, a former Lucent executive, as president and CEO. Even after the spin-off of Agilent, HP revenues in 1999 were $42 billion and the company employed 84,400 employees.

At the time of co-founder Bill Hewlett's death, in 2001, HP was focused on reducing the cost and complexity of information technology (IT) systems for business and on improving the overall technology experience of its customers. Following a history-making merger with Compaq Computer Corporation, in 2002, the company became a global technology giant serving more than one billion customers across 162 countries. HP's offerings spanned IT infrastructure, personal computing and access devices, global services, and imaging and printing.

In 2005, HP Chairman and CEO Fiorina was succeeded by Mark Hurd, former CEO of NCR Corporation, who was named by the board to serve as CEO and president. Hurd's leadership focuses on growing HP's businesses while lowering costs, building determination and excitement in the work force, realigning reporting structures, and returning the company to consistent profitability. Today the revitalized company continues on its march to become the world's leading IT company.

In 2007, HP is a Fortune 14 company with $97 billion in revenue and 156,000 employees, doing business in more than 170 countries. A technology solutions provider to consumers, businesses, and institutions globally, the company's offerings span IT infrastructure, global services, business and home computing, and imaging and printing. HP Labs continues to invent for the future by delivering breakthrough technology advancements in areas such as nanotechnology, color science, and social and economic systems.

HP continues to be a company fueled by progress and innovation and focusing on the desire to create valued experiences and better lives with technology. Because it has long held citizenship as a top priority, as relevant to the company as profits, HP also continues as a leading contributor to education and other important human needs in its communities.

From their start in a garage, which was listed in the National Register of Historic Places in 2007, Hewlett and Packard's legacy of humanistic management continues to evolve to meet the challenges of business in the 21st century. While embracing its rich heritage, Hewlett-Packard Company is blazing a path to a future full of opportunities.

The "HP Way," was described by Bill Hewlett as "the policies and actions that flow from the belief that men and women want to do a good job, a creative job, and that if they are provided with the proper environment they will do so."

Opportunity Knocks

He was destined to be great!
Sometimes the great ones will admit that luck had a lot to do with their success.

"It turns out that the early business relationship that was promoted by Steve Jobs with Apple made a really critical difference in the way that our company developed."

> — **Charles Geschke**
> **Founder, Adobe Systems**

"There's a lot to be said about being at the right place at the right time, and essentially, we were there. We didn't know it at the time, but that's what happened."

> — **David Packard**
> **Founder, Hewlett-Packard**

"When we started the company, we didn't realize that you could go off and build a nearly $5 billion company in 12 years. We actually had no clue that we were going to be successful. We had no idea how big the market was. We just came in every day, did the best we could, got a little lucky, worked really hard and had a little magic because we had the right group of founders, the right timing, the right marketplace, the right geography—the stars were all lined up."

> — **Scott McNealy**
> **Founder, Sun Microsystems**

"Great ideas still take a lot of hard work to turn into a reality. And in the case of hard work, a lot of hard work, a lot of money, and a lot of luck to supplement your vision."

> — **Larry Ellison**
> **Founder, Oracle Corporation**

"I was hanging posters at Stanford University, advertising for:
Wanted: programmer to help on exciting new software product.

I didn't know where to put them up. So, I walked into a building that looked like an engineering building and asked a group of students who were seated in a circle. ... one of the students said, 'I might be interested in that. Let me have one of those.' Well, that was Tom Proulx, the cofounder of Intuit. So, we met totally by chance."

> — **Scott Cook**
> **Founder, Intuit**

"Some are born great, some achieve greatness, and some have greatness thrust upon them."

> — **William Shakespeare**
> **Twelfth-Night**

Chapter 6: World War II Brings Science-Based Weapons to the Fore

Nazi Germany's shock troops, employing blitzkrieg tactics, had overrun most of Western Europe. Japan's forces, meanwhile, were rampaging through large parts of Asia. Most Americans believed the United States would have to fight.

In 1940, the British Royal Air Force and the German Luftwaffe were locked in the aerial battle of Britain. Despite the cruel punishment its people and cities were taking, Britain had a secret edge. It had developed radar, and the advent of the klystron — light enough to be put aboard aircraft — would later make the British system more workable. It arrived too late for employment in the air defense of Britain, but in time to help quell the menace of Nazi submarines. This technology symbolized the new science-based weapons the war was bringing to the fore, and it greatly aided Britain in beating off the U-boat assaults.

University Ave., Palo Alto

Under President Franklin Roosevelt's leadership, the United States supplied war materials to Britain and also to the Soviet Union after Germany turned on that former ally. America's scientists and engineers were mustered for an all-out effort to develop new weapons.

In December 1941, Japan bombed U.S. forces at Pearl Harbor with devastating effect, and attacked American and British bases in the Far East. Within days Congress declared the United States at war with Japan, Germany, and Italy.

Companies along the San Francisco peninsula quickly shifted from a preparedness to a war footing. Eitel-McCullough and Litton Engineering Laboratories geared up to produce vacuum tubes in unprecedented quantities. Kaar Engineering became a leading builder of two-way radios. Dalmo Victor developed military airborne radar equipment. Lenkurt built microwave telephone systems. In San Jose, Food Machinery and Chemical Corp., long a fabricator of agricultural spray pumps and cannery machinery, shifted operations to become a leading producer of tracked military vehicles.

Fred Terman at Stanford answered the call of his old MIT mentor, Vannevar Bush, to head the top-secret Radio Research Laboratory at Harvard University, eventually leading a corps of 800 scientists and engineers. The Army Signal Corps ordered Bill Hewlett to active duty again, this time

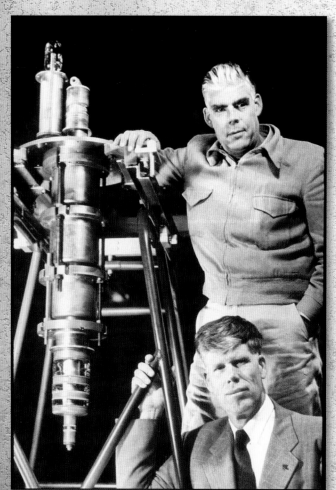

Varian Brothers with Klystron

1940	**1941**	**1942**			**1945**
Radar is developed.	The U.S. enters World War II after attack on U.S. fleet in Pearl Harbor.	The first nuclear reactor is activated.	The world's first computer (ENIAC) is created.	The U.S. defeats Japan in sea battle near Midway Island in the Pacific.	The U.S. drops the atomic bomb on the cities of Hiroshima and Nagasake.

Fred Terman

for the duration. Dave Packard managed their company's defense production after 1942, in the first plant Hewlett-Packard built on Page Mill Road.

Terman's lab personnel devised jamming devices, particularly a radar countermeasure known as chaff, and developed tunable receivers for detecting and analyzing radar signals. Some of the related manufacturing was assigned to HP, which also made proximity fuses that had only to be shot near, not strike, an enemy tank or plane to score a hit. These fuses gave the Allies an edge in both the air war and tank clashes like the Battle of the Bulge. The sophisticated radar countermeasures HP worked on were not completed by the war's end in August 1945, but they were ready when the Cold War began soon afterward. Atomic weapons dropped by the United States on Hiroshima and Nagasaki hastened Japan's surrender without the necessity to assault her homeland — an operation deemed likely to cause up to a million more U.S. casualties.

Clearly America's gamble on science-based weapons had paid off by helping the Allies to win the war and, despite the terrible costs of the conflict in lives and treasure, shortening its duration and reducing casualties.

While doing war work in the East, Terman, Hansen, the Varian brothers, Edward Ginzton and others learned from personal experience how Harvard and MIT managed their relations with Washington and how defense production firms such as Sperry operated. They acquired a taste for large-scale, project-oriented science. Stanford University had not played such a role in the long, grinding years of war. Many of its faculty had scattered, although one who remained on campus, physics Professor Paul Kirkpatrick, had developed the X-ray microscope in 1945. When peace finally came, it brought eagerness to reorganize for a new era — along with turbulence and shortages.

Terman was named dean of engineering in 1944, many months before he could return West. When he finally did come home, he had important new concepts in mind. He foresaw a rising tide of U.S. government support for science and technology, owing to their wartime successes. And he was convinced that his own field, electronics, was due to become even more essential in modern civilization. The Peninsula's World War II role in microwave tube production for radio and radar clearly was destined for further expansion, after a rocky readjustment to peacetime conditions.

An early signal of a fresh outlook on campus was the founding of Stanford Research Institute in 1946. SRI was created to do applied and contract research in conjunction with the university, with leading California businesses and industries among its sponsors. High hopes for this not-for-profit enterprise were not misplaced, for among SRI's accomplishments in subsequent years were such quantum jumps as magnetic ink character recognition (1955), ink-jet printing (1961), optical disk recording (1963), the mouse computer input device (1964), and the acoustic coupler/modem (1965). Companies hungry to develop these better mousetraps beat a path to SRI's doors in Menlo Park.

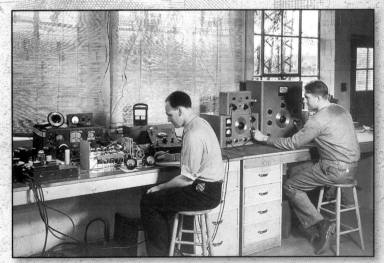

Hewlett-Packard's first post-garage shop

Nazi's report the death of Adolf Hitler.

Italian patriots execute Mussolini.

Germany surrenders to the Allies ending the war in Europe.

The forty year cold war between the U.S. and the Soviet Union begins.

Percy Spencer invents the microwave oven in the U.S.

1946
The United Nations General Assembly meets for the first time.

SRI built and operates this 150-foot radio reflector antenna located in the hills above Stanford University. Known locally as "The Dish", the antenna is used for satellite calibrations and spacecraft communications.

Since the organization's founding in 1946, SRI International has been at the forefront of Silicon Valley innovation. The independent, nonprofit research institute, begun by Stanford University and a group of business executives, was created to stimulate West Coast economic development after World War II. In 1970, SRI gained its independence from Stanford University, and in 1977, changed its name to SRI International. The Menlo Park-based firm's founding mission holds true today: SRI is committed to discovery and to the application of science and technology for knowledge, commerce, prosperity, and peace.

Known originally as Stanford Research Institute, SRI has focused its extensive R&D capabilities on nearly every area of industry, medicine, education, and government, including wide-ranging areas such as banking, robotics, entertainment, special education, atmospheric research, national defense, homeland security, and much more. Along the way, SRI's innovations have created new industries, billions of dollars in market value, and lasting benefits to people around the globe.

SRI's first researchers hit the ground running. In 1949 the institute held the nation's first symposium on air pollution. In the early 1950s, SRI recommended that Walt Disney select Anaheim, California, for his first theme park, Disneyland.

But that was only the beginning. By the mid-1950s, SRI was providing economic research and consulting services on an international level. For example, in 1955 it conceived of the National Council for Applied Economic Research for India and in 1957 cosponsored the International Industrial Conference, a summit that brought together hundreds of world leaders and CEOs from 50 countries— an important event SRI cosponsored for 40 years.

In addition to expanding its reach during the 1950s, SRI developed several breakthrough products. The Electronic Recording Machine, Accounting (ERMA) and magnetic ink character recognition (MICR) together revolutionized banking by enabling automatic check processing to replace laborious manual recordkeeping, inaugurating business process automation. Another breakthrough product, the Technicolor® electronic printing timer, reduced the time and expense of producing movie prints, allowing the film industry to bring color movies to audiences much faster.

Breakthroughs in the 1960s in computing, robotics, and communications cemented SRI's position as a worldwide innovation leader. The organization supported the growing interest in the upper atmosphere and outer space—the start of the decade saw the first man in space and the end of the decade saw another man walking on the moon—by building and operating for the U.S. government a 150-foot radio reflector antenna located in the hills above Stanford University. Known locally as "The Dish," the antenna is used today for satellite calibrations and spacecraft communications.

In the 1960s, the organization also laid the foundation for the personal computer revolution. SRI invented the computer mouse in 1964 and, in 1968, first publicly demonstrated the concept of "windows," hypertext, and videoconferencing, all of which have advanced how people work, learn, and communicate.

The new science of robotics was also greatly influenced by SRI expertise—in the institute's renowned Artificial Intelligence Center, researchers developed Shakey, the first mobile

SRI invented the computer mouse in 1964, laying the foundation for the personal computer revolution.

Since the 1960s, SRI has discovered and developed hundreds of drugs, including several now in clinical trials.

robot with the ability to reason about its surroundings. The institute was also instrumental in another first: In 1969, SRI was one of the first four computer nodes on the ARPANET, the small government network that preceded the Internet. Seven years later, SRI established the first connection among dissimilar networks—the wired ARPANET, SRI's wireless mobile packet radio network, and the Atlantic packet satellite network—which has been described as first true inter-networked computer connection.

Since the 1960s, drug discovery and healthcare have also benefited from SRI innovations. In the 1970s, SRI discovered Halofantrine, a malaria treatment that has saved countless lives. In the 1980s, SRI made pioneering developments in ultrasound that made it practical for clinical use. Today, SRI has several new drugs in development.

Connecting people and places has also continued to be a key focus. Until 1992, the institute served as the Network Information Center (NIC), the clearinghouse and support center for all computer hosts connecting to ARPANET and the Internet. SRI also developed a nationally used telecommunication system, called Deafnet, for the hearing impaired. And SRI's "signature pen" allowed computers to recognize handwritten words and symbols, including non-Roman alphabets such as Chinese.

In 1987, SRI acquired the David Sarnoff Research Center (now called Sarnoff Corporation) from General Electric. Sarnoff developed high-definition television, among many other commercial contributions.

SRI's breakthrough marketing tool, the Values and Lifestyles™ program, or VALS™, was an important innovation of the 1980s, helping advertisers and others determine why consumers make the purchasing decisions they do. The 1990s saw innovations in education, as well as continuing work in many other areas.

SRI was honored with a 1959 Academy Award® for its role in developing the Technicolor® electronic printing timer, which allowed the motion picture industry to release new movie prints quickly.

Sponsored by the National Science Foundation, SRI developed the TAPPED IN® learning environment, a virtual meeting place for K-12 educators that has allowed more than 16,000 users to take online courses as well as collaborate and participate in events. DynaSpeak® and EduSpeak®, SRI speech recognition engines, aid language translation and education in military, civilian, and business applications. And developments such as electroactive polymer "artificial muscle" for energy generation put SRI at the leading edge of tremendous advances in science and technology.

Since the turn of the new millennium, SRI has continued in its role as a premier research and development organization. Speech technology created by the institute enables U.S. soldiers overseas to communicate in real time with local citizens. The Centibots, descendants of Shakey, are an SRI-designed team of autonomous mobile robots that can explore, map, and survey unknown environments. SRI is helping the National Guard prepare soldiers for combat through a novel integration of live–virtual–constructive training systems. And ground- and foliage-penetrating radar that can find unexploded ordnance put SRI at the leading edge of tremendous advances in science.

SRI and Sarnoff also bring new technologies and products to market through technology licenses and spin-off ventures. Together, the organizations have created more than two dozen spin-offs, including three publicly traded companies. One of these is Intuitive Surgical, which commercialized SRI's novel, minimally invasive surgical robotics technology. Surgeons throughout the U.S., Europe, and Asia use Intuitive's da Vinci® Surgical System to help patients recover faster, with less pain and fewer complications.

SRI's novel, minimally invasive surgical robotics technology is being commercialized by Intuitive Surgical to help surgeons and patients around the world.

For 60 years and counting, government agencies, commercial businesses, and private foundations have turned to SRI for solutions to their most important problems. SRI applies a disciplined approach to innovation to succeed on every project it undertakes.

SRI continues its role as a premier research and development organization. SRI International has worked toward—and will continue to work toward—improving quality of life around the world.

Stanford University

Chapter 7: Postwar Era Ushers in Federal Support for University Research

Frederick Terman returned to Stanford University as dean of engineering in 1946. His belief that science and technology would gain new infusions of government support as a result of their wartime successes was soon borne out. Within a few months, the Office of Naval Research awarded Stanford a $225,000 annual contract for basic research.

This funding empowered Terman to shape new research plans. He set up three projects. The one in physics led to the discovery of nuclear magnetic resonance and the Nobel Prize for Felix Bloch in 1952 — the first in a long string of high honors for Stanford scientists. The chemistry project fizzled, but the electronics project led to creation of Stanford's Electronics Research Laboratories and, soon, a plan for developing a Stanford Linear Accelerator Center.

Russell and Sigurd Varian returned to the Bay Area in 1948 after their wartime stint with Sperry at Long Island, N.Y. Soon they joined Edward Ginzton, Marvin Chodorow, and other Sperry colleagues in forming Varian Associates. Initially the firm settled in San Carlos, where Sperry had had a prewar outpost. In addition to producing klystrons, Varian Associates developed applications of the linear accelerator and nuclear induction devices W.W. Hansen had pioneered at Stanford. Hansen mortgaged his house to give the company a just-in-time loan, and died soon afterward.

Initial Varian Associates products were based directly on Stanford-owned patents, and many of the associates were also Stanford faculty members. These close interties prompted Varian to seek a base closer to the university, and in 1950 the firm took the first lease of Stanford land designated for light industry, moving operations there in 1952-53.

Edward Ginzton at Varian

Soon after World War II ended, scientists at Ames Research Center turned their attention to understanding problems of high-speed flight. One outgrowth of this effort was the concept by Robert T. Jones of using swept-back wings. Later H. Julian Allen and Alfred J. Eggers Jr. developed the blunt-body concept for ballistic missiles and spacecraft re-entering Earth's atmosphere at tremendous velocities.

The Korean War began in mid-1950 and soon imparted a great surge to electronics industries. Poised for this growth with a full line of electronic measuring devices ready, Hewlett-Packard found its business and work force doubling every year. HP products were in high demand for electronics production and medical and military

1947
Dead Sea Scrolls discovered.

1948
The Berlin Airlift; (1948-49).

A Hindu fanatic assassinates Mohandas K. (Mahatma) Gandhi.

The transistor is invented.

1949
The U.S. and West European nations form the North Atlantic Treaty

Organization (NATO) for collective security.

- 42 -

Early Hewlett-Packard Employees assemble circuits

uses. Meanwhile, the war sent Office of Naval Research envoys straight to Fred Terman with a new proposal. Quickly, a new Applied Electronics Laboratory was built with Navy money and a gift from Hewlett-Packard. The lab ran on $450,000 a year in federal funding.

International Business Machines Corp., spurred by the Korean War, put its first large-scale electronic computer into production in New York State in 1952. Hoping to tap a new source of engineers in California, the company selected San Jose as home for a western research laboratory. Reynold Johnson, who had invented a test-scoring machine in 1937 and then managed IBM time clock and key punch developments, was assigned to head the project. Johnson and two assistants traveled west with a free hand to staff the new lab and choose what it would work on. Among the numerous projects begun in a former printing plant at 99 Notre Dame Avenue in San Jose, one entitled "Source Recording" moved to the fore. It was aimed to mechanize the handling of punched cards and eliminate awkward "tub files" that clerks had to staff. In fact, it ultimately reshaped the computer industry.

By early 1953, magnetic disks had been selected as the best medium for a random access memory. Digital magnetic recording was then primitive, and disks presented stability problems. An air head containing a magnetic read/write element met the need for constant head-to-surface spacing. To access stacked disks, IBM employed its first servo system. The RAMAC 305 made its debut in 1955, enabling businesses to process information right away rather than wait for a batch to pile up. Its disk file marked the birth of the direct access storage device industry. IBM set up a San Jose manufacturing plant, but kept the lab independent.

Meanwhile, on the small portion of Stanford lands earmarked for light industry, Eastman Kodak followed Varian as a tenant. This prompted Terman to object that Stanford ought not to host firms having no close relations with university purposes and research. His stand won him a role in the university's land development planning, and in 1953 the trustees junked a plan for extensive residential development and set up Stanford Industrial Park with over 650 choice acres to lease to high-technology enterprises.

The microwave tube era was still gathering momentum but a tiny device called the transistor was due to transform it. William Shockley had co-invented the transistor with John Bardeen and Walter Brattain at Bell Labs in 1947. Its first commercial use was in 1952 in a hearing aid. Soon afterward, transistors supplanted vacuum tubes in radios.

An epochal step in 1952 foreshadowed the advent of genetic engineering. Joshua Lederberg, then at the University of Wisconsin, discovered that viruses that attack bacteria can transmit genetic material from one bacterium to another.

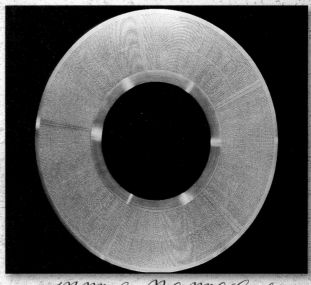

IBM first RAMAC disk

1949	**1950**		**1952**	**1953**	
Albert Einstein states his theory of gravitation.	Korean War; (1950-53).	Campaign for civil rights in the U.S. for African Americans; (1950's).	The hydrogen bomb undergoes tests.	DNA is discovered.	E.P. Hillary and native guide Tenzig climb Mt. Everest, the world's highest mountain.

Varian Medical Systems is the world's leading provider of equipment and software for treating cancer and other medical conditions with radiotherapy, brachytherapy, proton therapy, and radiosurgery. The company is also the largest independent supplier of X-ray tubes and flat panel digital X-ray image detectors for filmless imaging equipment used in medical, scientific, and industrial applications. Varian's high-energy X-ray imaging technology is used in cargo screening and non-destructive testing and inspection systems.

The Palo Alto-based company was founded under the name Varian Associates in 1948 by brothers Russell and Sigurd Varian and others, including a number of Stanford University researchers. The founders developed the klystron tube, which became the foundation for radar and microwave communications, and nuclear magnetic resonance (NMR) technology, which led to great advances in molecular research. The company went on to develop analytical instruments, vacuum products, and semiconductor manufacturing products. In 1999, after spinning off its instrument and semiconductor units, it was renamed Varian Medical Systems, a multinational organization focusing on products for radiotherapy, radiosurgery, and X-ray imaging. As of the end of 2006, the company had more than $1.6 billion in sales, and employed more than 4,200 employees in 56 sales and support offices around the world as well as in manufacturing and R&D operations in Canada, China, England, Finland, France, Germany, Switzerland, and the U.S.

More than 100,000 patients are now treated daily with Varian cancer treatment technology worldwide. Providing high-performing products that include linear accelerators and software for managing patient information, treatment planning, verification, delivery, and quality assurance, Varian technology offers patients advanced radiotherapy treatments, including SmartBeam™

The original Varian team (from left): Russell Varian, Sigurd Varian, Marvin Chodorow, Dorothy Varian, Richard Leonard, Esther Salisbury, Edward Ginzton, Fred Salisbury, Don Snow, and Myrl Stearns

intensity-modulated radiation therapy (IMRT); image-guided radio-therapy and radiosurgery (IGRT and IGRS); dynamic adaptive radio-therapy (DART™), and proton therapy. Simply put, the mission of the company's Oncology Systems business is to cure cancer.

More recently, Varian launched a line of advanced technology for treating cancer and disorders of the central nervous system with radiosurgery and neurosurgery. The company's leading-edge Trilogy® linear accelerator combines a powerful, highly focused radiation beam with advanced imaging capabilities to offer patients fast and effective image-guided radiosurgery that can be done on an outpatient basis.

Varian CEO Tim Guertin with Dick Levy, Chairman of the Board

The X-ray Products business, based in Salt Lake City, manufactures more than 400 types of X-ray tubes as well as the PaxScan® line of flat-panel digital X-ray image detectors for diagnostic imaging. The unit's manufacturing plant produces more than 22,000 tubes per year.

Varian makes safe, efficient, quiet-operating, long-lasting X-ray tubes that yield superior images. These tubes are designed to take the stress of spinning around a computed tomography (CAT) scan machine at a rate of up to three times per second.

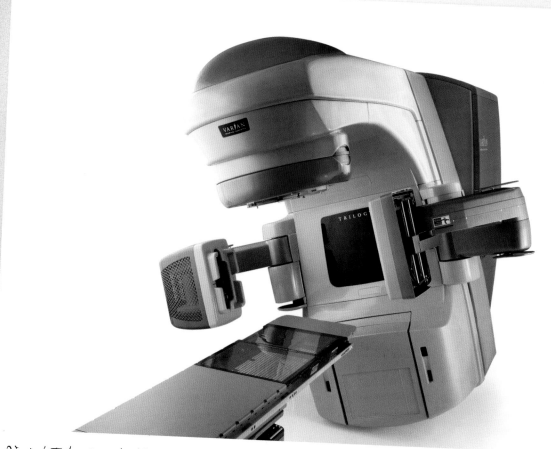

Varian's Trilogy® medical linear accelerator, introduced in 2003, combines imaging and treatment technology in a single unit, offering patients fast and effective image-guided radiosurgery that can be done on an outpatient basis.

Simply put, the mission of the company's Oncology Systems business is to cure cancer.

The Security and Inspection Products group is the market leader in high-energy X-ray linear accelerators for non-destructive testing and cargo screening. Varian's Linatron® X-ray accelerators are in use in cargo scanning systems at ports in over 35 countries around the world. The group's new Linatron K9™ accelerator makes it possible, for the first time, to build cargo-screening systems that can scan containers and automatically determine whether they contain weapons of mass destruction.

With CEO and president Tim Guertin at the helm, Varian Medical Systems is now building on nearly 60 years of innovation and excellence by pursuing new technologies and products that promise ever-higher levels of disease management, diagnostic imaging, and security.

Businesses and individuals, both domestic and international, seek out the widely recognized legal services of Ropers, Majeski, Kohn & Bentley (RMKB). This renowned Silicon Valley–based firm offers litigation and transactional services across a broad range of legal needs, in the areas of appellate law, business litigation, construction litigation, corporate law, employment counseling and litigation, entertainment law, environmental law and toxic tort liability, insurance coverage and bad faith, intellectual property, information technology and business process outsourcing, product liability, professional negligence, and real estate.

Founded in 1950 in Redwood City, California, the Firm today has grown to 115 attorneys in five offices.

Founded in 1950 by two local attorneys, Harold Ropers and Eugene Majeski, the firm has grown to 115 experienced attorneys and expanded to five offices: Redwood City, San Jose, San Francisco, Los Angeles, and New York; it also has an affiliated office located in Hong Kong. In addition to growing in size, the firm has grown in stature—RMKB has been recognized and featured in such publications as "Best Lawyers in America," and many of its senior members have been honored with membership in the American College of Trial Lawyers and the American Board of Trial Advocates. Most of the firm's partners hold the AV®-Peer Review Rating from Martindale-Hubbell.

The firm has also been recognized for its ability to enter cases late, to utilize its extensive trial experience in complex litigation, and to efficiently prepare and try matters successfully. As a sought-after legal force for more than half a century, Ropers, Majeski, Kohn & Bentley remains dedicated to providing its clients with superior, comprehensive services that meet their legal needs.

RMKB attorneys provide litigation and transactional services to clients in a wide variety of industries in the US and abroad.

Chapter 8: Peninsula Electronics Attain Critical Mass

Lockheed developed the submarine-launched Polaris missile

Events beginning about 1954 combined to impart critical mass to Peninsula electronics. The ICBM chapter of the arms race, the onset of the space race, the introduction of transistor technology, and moves to Stanford Industrial Park and nearby sites by many companies—among them several major start-ups—sent "smokeless" industrial growth surging.

Since World War II ended, the United States and the Soviet Union had been building on German rocket scientists' wartime achievements. In 1954, two developments—thermonuclear weapons and miniaturized, accurate inertial guidance systems—made intercontinental ballistic missiles (ICBMs) more feasible and more fearsome. America assigned a key strategic role to nuclear submarines carrying solid-propellant intermediate-range missiles.

Lockheed Aircraft moved its Missiles and Space Division (later renamed Company) from Burbank to Sunnyvale in 1956, and set up its research laboratory in Stanford Industrial Park. LMSC employment burgeoned as workers at the plant flanking Moffett Field built the U.S. Navy's Polaris missiles, first tested by 1958 and fired underwater by 1960.

Soviet launches of Earth-orbiting Sputniks in 1957 shocked Americans into frenzied efforts to catch up. Educational reforms began, and federal money poured into Santa Clara Valley science-based industry. In 1958, NASA—the National Aeronautics and Space Administration—was created. At Ames, renamed Ames Research Center, NASA took over the old NACA offices and wind tunnels. Its mission broadened beyond aeronautics to such areas as life sciences, space physics, astronomy, material sciences, and space project management.

Hewlett-Packard became the Industrial Park's flagship company in 1956, and David Packard joined the Stanford Board of Trustees and shared with Fred Terman the role of public spokesman for the land-use policy. By 1960 more than 40 companies occupied leased Stanford University land. In 1956 alone, ten companies started in Palo Alto. Many high-tech firms based elsewhere created western branches in the park.

One settler was William Shockley, back in his boyhood home town hoping to cash in on advanced transistors. Sponsored by Beckman Instruments, he formed Shockley Semiconductor Laboratories in 1956, and recruited a team of top-flight young scientists and engineers. Transistors had already begun to replace bulky vacuum tubes in electronic products, promising new reliability and reduced sizes. His protégés joined in celebrating that year when Shockley and his Bell Labs colleagues won the Nobel Prize for inventing the transistor. (For what ensued, please see the next chapter.)

Meanwhile, Ampex Corporation in Redwood City was making fast progress on another front. The company pioneered by Alexander Poniatoff, a Russian émigré, had married German tape-recording technology to its own small-engines skills. Its first big break came in 1947 when crooner Bing Crosby, who liked to pre-record his radio shows rather than perform live, ordered 20 sets. Broadcasters proved their reliability in 1948, and Ampex spurted. By 1955 Ampex marketed the first stereo home music system, and in 1956 a team led by Charles Ginsburg perfected

Presidential politics in 1950s

1954
U.S. Supreme Court unanimously rules racial segregation in public schools unconstitutional.

The U.S.S.R. opens the first nuclear power station.

Gregory Pincus and John Rock of the U.S. invent the contraceptive pill.

1955
The Warsaw Pact is signed.

Nautalis, the first atomic-powered submarine, undergoes sea tests.

1955
Vaccine against polio (salk vaccine) reported to be 80-90% effective.

the first videotape recorder. Unlike film, the electromagnetically made videotape needed no processing, and the television industry adopted it rapidly.

At Stanford, physics professor Arthur Schawlow had been working with Charles H. Townes in a study of how to create an optical version of Townes' maser (microwave amplification by stimulated emission of radiation). In 1958, they proposed a method in a published paper. Within a few years, several pioneering lasers (the L is for light amplification) were built, and new industrial operations such as Spectra-Physics of Mountain View and Coherent, Inc., of Palo Alto took wing.

Pontiaff and first video recorder

Among 1957's start-ups was Watkins-Johnson Company, co-founded by Stanford electrical engineering professor Dean A. Watkins, inventor of the helitron, a traveling-wave tube, and H. Richard Johnson, who had directed microwave tube research at Hughes Aircraft. W-J made its mark in defense electronics and semiconductor manufacturing equipment.

In 1955, Fred Terman became provost at Stanford, and extended his "steeples of excellence" thinking to fields beyond engineering. The university's run of Nobel laureates echoed this step. Willis Lamb shared the physics prize in 1955 for experimental work that spurred refinements in the quantum theories of electromagnetic phenomena. William Shockley, co-winner in 1956, later joined the faculty. Arthur Kornberg won the medicine prize in 1959, the year

Dr. Terman at Stanford

he moved to Stanford from Washington University of St. Louis, for discovering how DNA molecules are duplicated in the bacterial cell and for reconstructing the process in test tubes. Robert Hofstadter relocated to Stanford in 1950 and used its linear electron accelerator to measure and explore atomic nuclear structures. He shared the 1961 physics prize.

Hewlett-Packard purchased the Sanborn Company of Waltham, Massachusetts, in 1961, moving into medical instruments and putting its OK on mergers as a way of high-tech business life. Meanwhile, the microelectronics revolution had begun, and the invention of the integrated circuit would propel it headlong into the future.

1956

Suez crisis; Britain and France fail to regain control of the Suez Canal from Egypt.

First trans-Atlantic telephone cable developed.

1957

The U.S.S.R. launches the first orbiting satellite, Sputnik I.

The Treaty of Rome ushers in the EEC.

ow headquartered in Santa Clara, California, in the heart of Silicon Valley, National Semiconductor, one of the primary analog solutions companies, began life on the East Coast, in Danbury, Connecticut. Founded nearly 50 years ago, in 1959, National Semiconductor was established to provide silicon mesa transistors for second-generation computers.

But change wasn't long in coming. In 1967, after National purchased Santa Clara-based Molectro, a small integrated circuit company, the Connecticut Yankee put down new roots in the Santa Clara Valley, which was known at the time more for its orchards than for silicon. National was only the second major semiconductor manufacturer to locate in the region.

Led by former Fairchild Semiconductor manufacturing executive Charles Sporck, National's sales quickly increased following the company's restructuring from building transistors to a new product line of proprietary ICs. By the end of 1968, National had reached $11 million in sales and the following year opened plants in Europe and Malaysia. By 1971, as the semiconductor industry grew, microprocessors were added to National's line along with transducers and Datachecker point-of-sale systems. In 1975 the company introduced the first "talking" cash register, and by the end of the decade was world renowned for its analog technology, which bridges the gap between the digital world of ones and zeroes and the real world of light, sound, temperature, speed, and pressure.

During the 1980s, National built three wafer fabs to keep up with growing demand in the booming PC market. In 1983 it became the first Silicon Valley semiconductor company to achieve more than $1

Charles Sporck
President of National
Semiconductor from
1967 to 1991

Brian L. Halla
Chairman of the Board, Chief Executive Officer

billion in sales and continued its analog leadership by building on its large portfolio of intellectual property. The company also introduced the industry's first commercially available single-chip 32-bit microprocessor in 1984 and acquired Fairchild Semiconductor in 1987.

A stylized wafer shows the National worldmark.

In 1991, Gil Amelio took over the reins as National's CEO and reshaped National Semiconductor by overhauling manufacturing and carefully honing product markets. At the end of the decade, with the proliferation of information appliances, the company bought Cyrix for its integrated audio and video processor technology as well as seven other companies to build system-on-chips. The strategy paid off, with National once again providing leading technologies for moving and shaping information focused on three core businesses: analog, information appliances, and information infrastructure. In 2000, National positioned itself as the company whose products bring "The Sight and Sound of Information" to users.

Today, led by CEO Brian L. Halla, National provides more than 15,000 of those products. These include power management circuits, display drivers, audio and operational amplifiers, communication interface products, and data conversion solutions, which are found in state-of-the-art wireless handsets, displays, and a variety of broad electronics applications, including medical, automotive, industrial, and test and measurement. National's leading-edge solutions enhance customers' electronic-systems experiences by providing more energy efficiency, precision, portability, and better audio and video.

In the future, National plans to continue investing in new value-added analog products for its customers. It also is committed to investing in and supporting potential. Recently the company was recognized by *Electronics Weekly* for this commitment with the magazine's Investing in People Award, presented for National Semiconductor's effective engineering development program.

A manufacturing associate wears a "bunnysuit" while handling wafers at this 1200-degree Centigrade furnace.

For more than 45 years, Wilson Sonsini Goodrich & Rosati has been one of the driving forces of Silicon Valley. By anticipating the enormous potential of young, entrepreneurial companies in the early days of the Valley, helping them connect with venture capitalists, offering the legal counsel and representation they needed as they grew, and advising them on business strategy, Wilson Sonsini Goodrich & Rosati has become one of the most successful and influential law firms in the nation. Today, it is recognized as the premier provider of legal services to technology, life sciences, and growth enterprises worldwide, as well as to the investment banks and venture capital firms that finance them.

When the firm was founded in 1961, as McCloskey, Wilson & Mosher, founding partner John Wilson believed that a visionary Palo Alto law firm could grow in close partnership with local entrepreneurs. Wilson found a capable ally in Larry Sonsini, the first associate hired by the firm. During the late 1960s and into the 1970s, Sonsini led the firm's efforts to forge lasting relationships with rising technology companies, primarily in the semiconductor industry.

By 1978, the firm had established a reputation in the area of business most critical to the Valley's young, emerging companies: gaining access to the money needed to finance their growth. Pete McCloskey had left to serve in Congress and Roger Mosher had left to practice litigation in a smaller

Wilson Sonsini Goodrich & Rosati headquarters located in Palo Alto, California

firm. Wilson and Sonsini were joined on the masthead by corporate partners John Goodrich and Mario Rosati.

In the late 1970s and early '80s, the technology sector underwent major changes, and the firm's client base expanded to include companies capitalizing on semiconductor technology. In addition, the firm was perfecting the recipe for financing, structuring, and growing technology companies. Sonsini and his colleagues focused on assisting clients with initial public offerings (IPOs) and uniting promising entrepreneurs with venture capital firms. In the early 1980s, when the personal computer and software industries took off, the firm was perfectly positioned. By representing companies such as Apple, LSI, and Sun Microsystems in their IPOs, Wilson Sonsini Goodrich & Rosati cemented its reputation as the nation's leading law firm for emerging technology companies.

Left to right: John Goodrich, John Wilson, Mario Rosati, and Larry Sonsini.

The firm continued to grow by responding to the changing needs of successful entrepreneurs and by committing to represent large, mature companies as well. When shareholder class-action lawsuits began to proliferate in the 1980s, the firm built the nation's leading securities litigation defense capability for emerging growth companies. Later, it built similar strengths in intellectual property, antitrust, the life sciences, and other key areas. Notable recent transactions include the HP-Compaq merger and IPOs for Google, Pixar, and Netscape.

The firm also has shared the values of its entrepreneurial clients, prizing diversity and providing pro bono legal services to community groups throughout the nation.

Today, the firm has long eclipsed the borders of Silicon Valley: In addition to its Palo Alto headquarters, Wilson Sonsini Goodrich & Rosati has six offices in technology hubs across the nation. It also has established a strong international presence, opening an office in Shanghai, China, and cultivating thriving practices in such countries as India and Israel. Its 650 attorneys provide a full array of legal services to approximately 300 public and 3,000 private clients, ranging from start-ups to multibillion-dollar global corporations.

Shockley's traitorous eight

The high point of Shockley Semiconductor's existence may well have been the champagne breakfast to which William Shockley treated his brainy young work force after learning he would share the 1956 Nobel Prize in Physics.

Shockley's prize was for his development of the junction transistor, an improvement over the point-contact transistor that won Nobel co-honors for two Bell Labs scientists whose research he had overseen, Walter Brattain

and John Bardeen. Associates rated him outstanding at assessing scientific talent and defining a research aim. But he had never run a company and, as David Packard said, after being asked how to hire a secretary and where to buy pencils, "Shockley didn't know the first thing about it." Some of his team questioned his priorities. Worse, they resented his treating them like children, using a lie detector test to try to find an information leak, and keeping an engineer standing for quite a while after reporting a lab discovery—Robert Noyce in one case—while he phoned someone at New Jersey's Bell Labs to assess its value.

By September 1957, eight of the young stars found they could no longer stomach Shockley's heavy-handed management. The group had chosen Noyce, Shockley's favorite, as its leader. Other members included Jean Hoerni, a Cal Tech chemist with two doctorates; Victor Grinich, a former SRI researcher; Julius Blank; Eugene Kleiner, a General Electric manufacturing engineer (now a prominent venture capitalist); Gordon Moore, who had grown up in San Mateo County before working for the Applied Physics Laboratory at Johns Hopkins University; Jay Last, an expert in photo optics from Corning Glass Works; and metallurgist Sheldon Roberts. Noyce had previously been with Philco-Ford.

Resigning, they decided to stick together and seek backing as a group. They worked in their garages and living rooms until Arthur Rock, then with a Boston investment firm, found a Connecticut company, Fairchild Camera and Instrument, that was willing to bankroll them as a division. Fairchild Semiconductors eventually made Mountain View its base, but early employees were still in a nondescript tilt-up at 844 E. Charleston Road, Palo Alto, in 1959 when Robert Noyce led them in inventing the first commercially practicable

William B. Shockley

1958
Development of the heart pacemaker; (implants begin in the 1960's).

1960
Theodore Maiman of the U.S. constructs laser.

Martin Luther King, Jr. leads civil rights protests in the U.S.; (1960's).

1961
The Berlin Wall is built to divide East Germany and West Germany.

Russian Yuri Gagarin is the first human in space and the first to orbit the earth.

The female oral contraceptive pill is marketed.

integrated circuit. Earlier, Jean Hoerni had contributed the planar process for deposition on silicon chips.

The eight recruited Ed Baldwin from Hughes Semiconductor to "provide seasoned management." Fairchild was still a newborn when Baldwin and the team he brought suddenly departed and founded Rheem Semiconductor Inc. They were charged with kidnapping Fairchild's trade secrets, a point that became minor once the integrated circuit reached the market. Rheem was sold within two years. However, the pattern for defections, at times with key technology, had been extended.

Transistors produced with Fairchild's mesa silicon planar processes won big orders first from IBM and later from the Minuteman I missile program. Fairchild Camera and Instrument exercised its option to buy out the founding group for $3 million, paying the founders $250,000 each in stock. After that, the parent company guarded its stock tightly and Noyce, now running the profitable division, found himself short of incentives to use in persuading talented associates not to go seek their own fortunes elsewhere.

Of the eight founders, Hoerni, Kleiner, and Roberts left first, in 1961, to found Amelco, which was bought by Teledyne Semiconductor in 1972. Four other Fairchild men quit to start Signetics, now owned in part by the Dutch firm, Philips Electronics. Despite the departures, Fairchild was big and important enough to lure many of the men revered today as semiconductor industry icons: Charles Sporck, Don Valentine, Andrew Grove, Tom Bay, Mel Phelps, Jerry Sanders, Marshall Cox, Bernie Marren, Floyd Kvamme and Bob Widlar, a peerless designer of analog linear circuits whose antics and independence became legendary.

Michael S. Malone, writing about Fairchild in his book *The Big Score*, called it a "corporate vocational school" for the young geniuses in its ranks. "Here they could screw up without serious repercussions—after all, nobody else knew how the job was done either—and learn from their mistakes." ... At Fairchild Semiconductor, he said, "the freewheeling, throttle-to-the-firewall business style of Silicon Valley [was] forged, its best-known personalities formed."

Charles Sporck

In the middle '60s, with Noyce promoted to group vice president and Charlie Sporck the general manager, Fairchild ran into trouble delivering products on time. Widlar and his linear team departed. Then, early in 1967, Sporck jumped to National Semiconductor, taking four executives with him—a blow from which the company never fully recovered. Rivals Motorola and Texas Instruments both passed Fairchild in sales and profits. Personnel left in droves. Finally, in June 1968, Bob Noyce and Gordon Moore announced that they were going. Andy Grove soon followed. Fairchild hired C. Lester Hogan from Motorola, and he brought a squad of suntanned Arizonans with him to boss the place. That and the firing of marketing ace Jerry Sanders destroyed what morale was left. Although Fairchild prospered into the '70s, it was a wounded giant. New companies formed by its former stars—Intel, National Semiconductor, and Sanders' Advanced Micro Devices—captured the cutting edge of semiconductor progress.

Jerry Sanders

Original Siliconix facility at 1140 West Evelyn Avenue, Sunnyvale, California circa 1962.

In March 1998, Vishay Intertechnology acquired the semiconductor business group of TEMIC, which included 80.4% of Siliconix, as well as Telefunken. This acquisition brought with it not just facilities, people, and product lines but also a piece of local California history. Founded in 1962, Siliconix is one of the oldest corporate names in Silicon Valley. By coincidence, Vishay was founded the same year as Siliconix.

Siliconix was the brainchild of Frances and Bill Hugle, research scientists at a Westinghouse semiconductor facility in Newport Beach. The initial investors for the company were EECO (Electronic Engineering Company of California) and the Baldwin Piano Company, which was a former employer of the Hugles and one of the first companies to license Western Electric's original transistor technology.

Dr. Richard Lee was chosen as general manager of Siliconix. Previously, he had established the first applications group at Texas Instruments and co-authored the industry's first paper on the integrated circuit. Eventually named as Siliconix president, Lee was succeeded by Richard Kulle in 1990 and by Dr. King Owyang in 1998. The company opened for business in Sunnyvale on March 5, 1962, and began occupying its present location—in what was then an unincorporated area of Santa Clara County—in August 1969.

Aerial view of the Siliconix facility circa 1993.

Siliconix's first products were junction field-effect transistors, or JFETs, which are low-noise devices used to switch and sense analog signals in applications like sample-and-hold circuits and operational amplifiers. The company shipped its first IC product, a diode-transistor-logic device (DTL), in February 1963. Analog switches and multiplexers, which Siliconix was the first company to introduce (in 1967 and 1968, respectively), are another product line that has continued to evolve with smaller packages and lower operating voltages.

Siliconix has a worldwide reputation for innovation in power semiconductor silicon technology and packaging. Its power devices fall into two categories: power MOSFETs (metal oxide

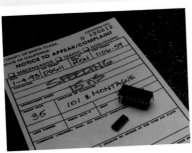

Publicity photo for the DG61X series of high-speed, low-glitch analog switches introduced by Siliconix in 1993. Siliconix invented the analog switch in 1967.

semiconductor field-effect transistors)—which are used to switch power—and power ICs, which can switch, convert, and control power in various ways, depending on the device and upon the application.

Vishay Siliconix packaging inventions have been introduced on a regular basis and include LITTLE FOOT®, the thermally enhanced PowerPAK®, the chipscale MICRO FOOT®, and PolarPAK®, the first double-sided cooling power MOSFET packaging technology to emerge as an industry standard.

Siliconix was the first in the industry (in 1993) to introduce power MOSFETs based on a Trench technology that allows a smaller area of silicon to efficiently handle a larger amount of current. Beginning with an 8 million transistor cells per square inch technology, successive generations of TrenchFETs have raised this density level—which translates directly into improved device performance—to 300 million cells per inch. Vishay Siliconix power IC devices complement power MOSFET products and work together with them in many cases to create the most efficient solutions on the market for powering computer, consumer, and fixed telecom systems.

In 2005, Vishay made a successful tender offer for the remaining 19.6% of Siliconix shares not included in the March 1998 acquisition.

Cover of the Siliconix MOSPOWER Design Catalog issued in January 1983. Siliconix is credited with having introduced the first power MOSFET in 1976.

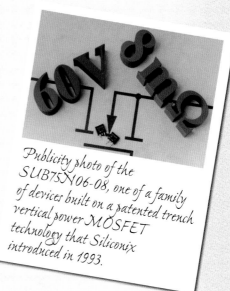

Publicity photo of the SUB75N06-08, one of a family of devices built on a patented trench vertical power MOSFET technology that Siliconix introduced in 1993.

White patch in center of the frame is building site of Siliconix facility at U.S. 101 and Montague in October 1968. The original 30-acre Siliconix property was a former pear orchard.

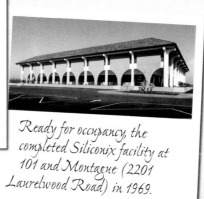

Ready for occupancy, the completed Siliconix facility at 101 and Montague (2201 Laurelwood Road) in 1969.

Syntex at work

During the mid-1960s, two federally funded Peninsula facilities pushed research deep into the atom and far beyond Earth's airy envelope. Other trends of the era included the buildup of a world-class medical center, moves to the south by burgeoning semiconductor firms, and the arrival of a major biotechnology company.

Syntex Corporation, which had been founded in Mexico, opened a research lab in Stanford Industrial Park in 1964. Soaring on the popularity of the birth control pill it introduced that year, Syntex added production space. Carl Djerassi, principal developer of the pill, joined the Stanford chemistry faculty. Syntex research director Alejandro Zaffaroni in 1968 founded Alza Corporation, which offered skin patches and other new drug delivery methods.

NASA's Ames Research Center began origin-of-life research in 1964, creating "building blocks" of life and charting many steps in the chemical evolution of life. In 1965, launchings began of four spacecraft, the Pioneer 6 through 9 series, to circle the Sun and study solar wind and cosmic rays. In 1989, Pioneer 6—still operating—became history's longest-lived spacecraft, continuing to send back data with an 8-watt Watkins-Johnson amplifier, a traveling-wave tube that was designed to last only three-plus years but instead was still operating after more than 20 years. Other Ames projects included Biosatellites 1, 2, and 3, which flew plants, insects, fertilized eggs, and a space ape known as Ham in orbit and returned them to Earth, testing the effects of weightlessness on living systems.

In contrast to tiny spacecraft traveling immense distances to explore space beyond Earth orbit, the Stanford Linear Accelerator Center applies tremendous energies to pry open the secrets of tiny particles inside the atom. SLAC was founded in 1962 and in 1966 began research at its two-mile-long electron "gun" in the foothills west of Menlo Park. Large klystron tubes initially speeded the electron beams to energies of 20 billion volts by the time they struck research targets. By 1968, the first evidence was discovered for quarks, the smaller, more fundamental objects within the proton and neutron that are constituents of the atomic nucleus. Richard Taylor of SLAC and two MIT scientists, Jerome Friedman and Henry Kendall, ultimately shared the 1990 Nobel Prize in physics for their quark work. Stanford University operates SLAC for the U.S. Department of Energy.

Stanford's medical school, a San Francisco fixture for many decades, moved in 1959 to the new Stanford Medical Center, straddling the line between Palo Alto and the university. Although some senior faculty members had bitterly opposed the move, it opened the way for more productive collaboration between faculty members in varied scientific fields. Physicians

Stanford Linear Accelerator

1964
U.S. Civil Rights Act bans racial discrimination in federal funding and employment.

Chemotherapy treatment for illness, particularly cancer, is developed.

1965
Malcolm X, African-American Muslim leader and activist, is shot and killed.

Watts Riots in Los Angeles, California.

Vietnam War; U.S. intervention ends in humiliating withdrawal of U.S. troops; (1965-75).

1966
Indira Gandhi is the prime minister of India.

Pioneer Satellite

broke fresh ground with the help of new scientific instruments invented and developed at Stanford—linear accelerators, lasers, computer programs, miniaturized instruments made possible by microelectronics.

As the 1960s unfolded, big news kept emerging from the medical center: the first open-heart surgery in 1960, initial "exports" of Stanford-developed linear accelerators for cancer treatment in late 1962, use of lasers to weld detached retinas (led by clinical faculty members Milton Flocks and Christian Zweng of the Palo Alto Medical Clinic), surgical cures of "blue baby" heart defects by Norman Shumway and colleagues, development by researcher Judith Pool of a much superior technique for extracting the blood fraction needed to prevent bleeding in hemophiliacs, installation of the medical school's first computing facility, and, on January 6, 1969, the first heart transplant in an adult patient in the United States, performed by Shumway, Edward Stinson, Eugene Dong, and colleagues.

Palo Alto and Stanford, partners since 1921 in operating a community hospital, went their separate ways in mid-1968 when the university bought out the city's share of their joint hospital. Though now at an end, the city's willingness to shoulder the rare municipal burden of owning a hospital had helped to create a high-ranked modern medical community.

Meanwhile, the 1960s had become the first great era of computers—primarily large computers built to run on IBM software, their operation much enhanced by the disk drives being improved constantly at the San Jose laboratory.

On the industrial front, development of semiconductors was surging. After camping in Palo Alto for a time, Fairchild Semiconductor had made its permanent home in Mountain View. This marked the start of a movement to the south that at length shifted most semiconductor production to Sunnyvale, Santa Clara, and San Jose. That trend was accompanied by a lessening of Stanford University's influence in that aspect of microelectronics, at least for a time. On the whole, output gained momentum, not only in semiconductors but also in ancillary out-sourcing activities, such as printed circuits and crystal growing, and in products for the armed forces: microwave tubes, avionics, and advanced radars.

By 1966 the Midpeninsula was widely recognized as America's largest microelectronics concentration. Two years later, Ampex, which had plunged into consumer products, began to see storm clouds on the horizon.

Linear-Electronic Accelerator for treating Retinoblastoma, a form of eye cancer.

1967
First successful human heart transplant surgery.

Assassination of South African prime minister Hendrik Verwoerd.

1968
Soviet troops enter Prague and end "Prague Spring" where Czechoslo-

vakia was trying to initiate reforms.

Civil rights leader Martin Luther King is assassinated.

Can you imagine a world without microchips? Yet as recently as the late 1960s, only a handful of pioneering companies were exploring this world-changing technology. And, one of those pioneers was Applied Materials, Inc.

Founded on November 10, 1967, Applied was started with seed money from local investors. Today it is the global leader in nanomanufacturing technology solutions with a broad portfolio of innovative equipment, service and software products for the fabrication of semiconductor chips, flat panel displays, solar photovoltaic cells, flexible electronics and energy efficient glass. With net sales in 2006 of over $9 billion and approximately 14,000 employees worldwide, it is the leading equipment supplier to the world's major technology manufacturers.

During the semiconductor industry's early years, manufacturers designed and built most of their own equipment. That changed with Applied's original engineering team's vision to supply fabrication systems to the industry and develop the company's first complete chemical vapor deposition (CVD) reactor, the AMV 300.

In the early years, Applied Materials began expanding globally. Then, in 1975, the entire semiconductor industry was hit by a severe recession. Within a year, Applied Materials was facing serious financial problems. Under the guidance of a new president, James C. Morgan, the company phased out several unprofitable products, closed subsidiaries, and returned its focus exclusively on the semiconductor equipment industry. The impact was immediate: Within one year the company recorded a 17% increase in sales.

In 1987, Applied Materials introduced the Precision 5000 CVD, a new revolutionary system that featured single-wafer, multi-chamber processing that could handle the new larger and more complex microchips. This technology

Applied Materials is the leading manufacturer of equipment used to create virtually every new microchip. Their machines are used in cleanrooms around the world. Above, employees work with the machines in the company's Maydan Technology Center.

established the company as the undisputed leader in single-wafer, multi-chamber fabrication architectures.

In the 1990s, the company saw further product expansion, including a move to supply flat panel display equipment, and a broader move to serve customers in Asia. By the late 1990s, the industry was hit with a triple wave of challenges: shrinking transistor sizes; the introduction of new, difficult-to-work-with materials; and a shift to larger wafers. Applied Materials engineers quickly enabled the company to be among the first semiconductor equipment makers to ship 300mm production systems to customers.

In 2003, Mike Splinter was named president and chief executive officer, as well as member of the Board of Directors of Applied Materials. He has focused the Company on expanding its leadership with a strong growth strategy by increasing market share and offering a breadth of products and service solutions.

In 2003, Mike Splinter, a veteran of the semiconductor industry, was named president and CEO, while Jim Morgan continued as chairman of the board of directors. Under Splinter's leadership, Applied Materials has reported solid financial results, achieved significant operational improvements, and continued to gain market share with its technology portfolio and new products.

No other chip equipment company has the breadth of products that Applied Materials offers as it enables its customers to produce virtually every new microchip, LCD flat panel display, and, in the near future, solar cells that will more cleanly power the world. The company's vision is to be the global leader in nano-manufacturing technology solutions and to offer a trusted path to superior results.

Through its commitment to diversity and corporate responsibility, Applied Materials earns top rankings on numerous prestigious lists, including: *Fortune* magazine's "America's Most Admired Companies" and CRO magazine's "100 Best Corporate Citizens."

The new face of solar, Applied Materials' executive team leading the company's entry into the rapidly growing solar photovoltaic equipment market. From left to right: Charlie Gay, Vice President, General Manager, Solar Business Group, Mike Splinter, President and Chief Executive Officer, Mark Pinto, Senior Vice President, Chief Technology Officer, General Manager, Energy and Environmental Solutions.

or nearly 40 years, Intel Corporation has been at the forefront of silicon innovation. Today it is the world leader in developing technologies, products, and initiatives to continually advance how people work and live.

Intel's early history is legendary. The company was established in 1968 by Robert N. Noyce, cofounder of the integrated circuit, and Gordon E. Moore, a colleague of Noyce's from Fairchild Semiconductor, to make semiconductor memory more practical and affordable. The pair quickly won the backing of venture capitalist Art Rock, who raised $2.5 million in less than two days. Because the name Moore Noyce was already trademarked by a hotel the two called their startup Intel, short for "integrated electronics."

Soon after Intel's founding, a third visionary joined the team: Andrew S. Grove, a Hungarian émigré who had played a critical role in the development of metal oxide semiconductor (MOS) large scale integrated (LSI) technology. Not long after that, top engineers Ted Hoff, Federico Faggin, and Stan Mazor joined the group. In late 1969, when a Japanese calculator manufacturer, Busicom, asked the new company to design 12 custom chips for one of its products, the innovative Intel team came up with a groundbreaking solution: one chip that could do the work of 12.

Robert Noyce

Andy Grove

Gordon Moore

Nine months later, the Intel 4004 was first produced, a 1/8-inch by 1/6-inch chip that contained 2,300 MOS transistors. This "computer on a chip" was the world's first microprocessor, with all the power of the 3,000-cubic-foot ENIAC computer.

In 1980 the 4004 was followed by the 8080, which was chosen as the central

Paul Otellini, president and CEO of Intel Corp., displays the new Intel® Core™ 2 Duo processor, during the launch event at Intel headquarters in Santa Clara, Calif.

Intel Headquarters

processing unit of IBM's first personal computer. In 1985 Intel introduced its next-generation Intel386™ microprocessor, and in 1993 the company's focus on R&D and manufacturing expertise resulted in the renowned Pentium microprocessor, whose descendants power performance-intensive applications today. Intel's groundbreaking achievements continue in the new century. In January 2006, the company announced it had designed what is believed to be the first fully functional SRAM (static random access memory) chip using 45-nanometer (nm) logic technology. Then, just a year later, Intel began to implement an innovative combination of materials that drastically reduced transistor leakage, improving energy efficiency, and significantly increasing performance in its 45nm process technology. Intel now uses a new material based on the element hafnium instead of silicon with a property called "high-k" for its transistor gate dialectric, and a new combination of metals for the transistor gate in portions of the millions of transistors inside a multi-core computer chip, which is about the size of a postage stamp. According to Gordon Moore, the move to hafnium-based high-k and metal gate materials "marks the biggest change in transistor technology since the introduction of polysilicon gate MOS transistors in the late 1960s."

Intel's new 45nm processor technology is now in production for more than 15 products in its next-generation family of computer chips. With more than 400 million transistors for dual-core processors and more than 800 million for quad-core, these next generation of Intel Core 2 chips provide greater performance, power-management capabilities, higher core speeds, and larger caches for desktop, mobile, workstation, and enterprise computers.

And more milestones are ahead including a 32 nanometer (nm) technology with transistors so small that more than 4 million of them could fit on the period at the end of a sentence on a printed page. "Intel has a long history of translating technology leaps into tangible benefits that people appreciate," said Bill Holt, vice president and general manager of the Intel Technology and Manufacturing Group. That forward-looking ethic is reflected in Intel's Leap ahead™ call to action, inspiring continuing commitment to moving silicon technology forward.

Intel 8080 chip and wafer

Originally known as LSI Logic because it provided computer-designable integrated circuits in the form of high-performance logic arrays to the electronic data-processing, military, and telecommunications markets, newly named LSI is today a leading provider of custom and standard ICs, adapters, systems, and software that power innovative solutions for data storage, networking, and telecommunications applications.

Wilfred J. Corrigan, founder, LSI Logic.

LSI was founded in early 1981 by Wilfred J. Corrigan, who created the application-specific integrated circuit (ASIC) market in the semiconductor industry. As one of the pioneers of the fabless semiconductor model, the company employed 46 people by the end of the first year at a leased fabrication facility in Santa Clara, California. At the same time, the company entered into what officials described as the "first fully cooperative semiconductor development program involving U.S. and Japanese companies." That program was a joint venture with Toshiba Corporation to develop a line of advanced semi-custom circuits.

By early 1983, LSI employed 120 people in its Milpitas, California, corporate headquarters and by the end of the year went public with the largest amount raised by a company until that time. At the end of the decade the company introduced the industry's first cell-based custom ASIC capable of integrating 200,000 gates on a single chip—an enormous advance over the company's initial IC, which had 1,782 gates.

In 1990 LSI introduced a high-performance video chip set for use in video teleconferencing terminals, color faxes, cameras, and other applications that require the rapid compression and decompression of images. That year it also completed its 10,000th design. In 1991 the company stimulated early interest in HDTV by being the only company selected to work with a major Japanese firm to reduce the size, cost, and complexity of HDTV decoders. The following year LSI introduced its CoreWare® approach to system-level integration, which involves stitching together industry-standard architectures, intellectual property, and a customer's proprietary logic for single-chip solutions.

The company's next innovation ushered in the system-on-chip era—in 1993 LSI introduced a .5-micron ASIC product family that could integrate up to 9,000,000 transistors on a single chip. At that point LSI went from being an ASIC supplier to a leading provider of complete system solutions. The

A few of the 1994 LSI engineers involved in developing the Sony Entertainment PlayStation CPU.

company's system-on-chip capabilities became a key element in Sony's PlayStation video games, which spawned the multi-million dollar video game industry.

Over the years, LSI has acquired a number of companies that have fueled its growth, including Symbios, a key element in LSI's storage systems and storage semiconductor businesses. Other acquisitions enabled LSI to consolidate its product offerings into four main areas: consumer electronics, communications, storage components, and storage systems.

When LSI Logic merged with Agere Systems in April 2007 to become the new LSI, the merged company became a more focused innovator of semiconductors and systems for storage and networking applications. LSI now holds more than 10,000 issued and pending U.S. patents.

Today, LSI is a leading innovator of core technologies and solutions that bring people and information together.

440 CERAMIC LEADED CHIP CARRIER (DZ)
Cavity Up
Flat Lead Configuration
20 mil Lead Pitch

144 CERAMIC PIN GRID ARRAY (FE)
Cavity Down
100 mil Pin Pitch

288 CHIP-ON-TAPE (48 mm) (TQ)
0.25 mm Outer Lead Pitch
Also available in 35 mm
and 70 mm sizes

304 METAL QUAD FLAT PACK (WT)
Cavity Up
0.5 mm Pin Pitch
Body Size: 40 mm

LSI chips from the 1990s

Customers should come first, at every stage of a company's activities. This customer-driven approach to doing business was at the core of AMD's founding in 1969 and remains the central focus of the company's policy today. States CEO and chairman Dr. Hector Ruiz, "Customer-centric innovation is the pre-eminent value at AMD. It is our reason for being and our strategy for success."

That success wasn't assured when former CEO Jerry Sanders and seven colleagues left Fairchild Semiconductor to start their own business. It took the group a year to overcome a stock market dip and raise $1,505,000 from doubtful venture capitalists. But Sanders and company understood that tremendous silicon-based advances were being made throughout the industry, including the first mini-computer and the first modem, and that customers needed a steady supply of the highest quality electronics in order to succeed. From his experience as an engineer and a worldwide marketing director at Fairchild, Sanders knew many of the electronic-equipment manufacturers personally and wanted to help them meet the new challenges.

W.J. (Jerry) Sanders, III
AMD Founder and Chairman Emeritus

"Customers should come first, at every stage of a company's activities."

–Dr. Hector Ruiz, CEO

AMD began by retooling existing products to make them more efficient and faster. Its first revenues came in 1970 from a 4-bit shift register. As the company added to its line, it also offered a plus, testing all of its products—even the simplest ones—at the company's own expense, according to strict military standards. The customers came and the company expanded, opening an assembly plant in Malaysia and increasing the size of its headquarters in Sunnyvale. By the end of its fifth year, AMD was manufacturing more than 200 products, many of them proprietary, and had close to $25.5 million in annual sales.

By the mid 1970s, the demand for microprocessors and memory products was growing as developers put semiconductor technology to new uses in consumer and business products. Great changes in computing, in particular, were taking place as people moved from large mainframe computers to personal desktop models. To help its customers stay ahead of the curve, AMD continued to focus on their needs, working to improve product performance, reduce costs, and shorten customers' time to market.

One of the ways the company did this was by launching its first memory product, the Am9102 RAM chip. In 1975 AMD also developed a reverse-engineered version of the 8080A standard processor, which gave the market a competitive alternative and brought AMD into the microprocessor field. The introduction of the Am2900 family of bit-slice processors greatly enhanced design capability and enabled companies to differentiate their products. Despite the recession in 1974 and 1975, AMD increased its business to $168 million.

The beginning of the new decade saw personal computing going mainstream and saw AMD supporting the explosive growth with high-quality x86 processor alternatives. To meet demand, AMD added more fabrication space as well as made significant investment in research and development. The company also introduced INT.STD.1000, the industry's highest manufacturing quality standard of the time.

By the end of the 1980s, AMD had begun work on its Submicron Development Center, where process-technology innovations would be developed throughout the 1990s. These innovations, which affect manufacturing before, during, and after the process, have kept AMD's manufacturing costs low as well as enabled the company to bring exciting technical advances to its customers ahead of their competitors.

The early 1990s also saw change in AMD's approach to the market. To offer more diverse solutions to its customers, the company broadened its focus into "spheres of influence": programmable logic devices, high-performance logic devices, high-performance memory, networking and communication chips, and PC-compatible microprocessors. After a long legal battle, it broke the monopoly on the x386 chip and shipped more than one million units of its Am386 processor family. In 1993 it began shipping its next-generation Am486 processors, affording customers even greater opportunities for innovation and cost savings.

Hector de J. Ruiz, Ph.D., Chairman of the Board and Chief Executive Officer

Dual-Core AMD Opteron™ processor

Throughout the 1990s, AMD continued to be a leader in the manufacture of integrated circuits, ranking high in each of its core business areas. It also continued to innovate, introducing, in 2000, a new 1.8-volt, 32-megabit flash memory product that allowed cell phone manufacturers to offer leading-edge features such as global positioning and electronic organizers.

The year 2000 saw another notable change—the appointment of a new president and COO, Dr. Ruiz. His expertise in process technology and leading market- and customer-focused businesses put AMD in a position of strength as the economy slowed and the technology bubble burst. In fact, in 2001 AMD's performance greatly exceeded that of the industry.

To keep the company strong, in 2002 Dr. Ruiz announced a new business philosophy—the "connected business model," in which companies, customers, and partners build relationships and are invested in each other. To put the new approach into effect, AMD opened a developer center to help its partners speed their development and validation processes for products built with AMD technology. It also entered into a joint venture with the China Basic Education Software Company to develop AMD technology-based PCs to support and assist educators and students in China.

The year 2003 saw another tremendous step forward for AMD: the availability of the first solution to extend the industry-standard x86 architecture to 64-bit computing. AMD's Opteron processor provides its customers with greater performance and simplified 64-bit computing and resulted in a groundbreaking alliance with Sun Microsystems. Its Athlon 64 processor, the first Windows-compatible 64-bit processor, provides unparalleled performance through technology that enables both 32-bit and 64-bit computing. Dirk Meyer, AMD's current president and COO, and Fred Weber, former CTO, played essential leading roles in the development of AMD's extraordinary 64-bit technology.

Now, after nearly four decades in business, AMD continues to innovate and to advance the digital age. But the company doesn't believe in improving technology for technology's sake. Just as it did at its founding, AMD is committed to helping its customers solve real-world problems. The company is now designing far-reaching computing solutions in support of its "50x15 Initiative," a bold commitment to bring affordable Internet access and computing capability to 50% of the world's citizens by the year 2015.

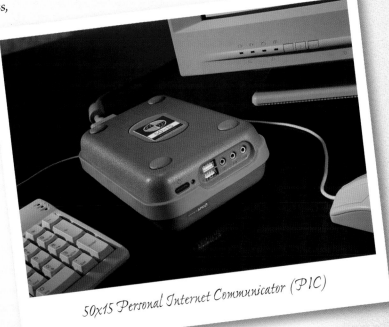

50x15 Personal Internet Communicator (PIC)

Chapter 11: An Era of Discovery—Moon, Microprocessors, and Gene Manipulation

"That's one small step for a man, one giant leap for mankind," said astronaut Neil Armstrong as he set foot on the Moon. This great U.S. achievement in 1969—thanks in considerable measure to theoretical work, flight simulation, and other NASA/Ames research—demonstrated America's recovery of the aerospace initiative. As the '70s unfolded, NASA/Ames guided the second and third Pioneer series explorations of the outer reaches of the solar system.

Meanwhile, the art of packing more and more circuitry onto a fingernail-size silicon chip steadily grew more amazing. When Robert Noyce and Gordon Moore founded Intel Corporation in 1968 (and Arthur Rock raised $5 million in start-up capital for them in 30 minutes on the telephone), they decided to focus on a little-contested part of the market:

Early Intel 8086 microprocessor

memory. In 1969 they were producing an 1101 256-bit static RAM (random access memory) for 21 cents per bit. By 1993, that price had been reduced to $.0000029 per bit in an 8-megabit flash chip—just one of Intel's many successes. The phenomenon of ever denser circuits at ever dwindling cost gained expression as "Moore's Law:" memory capacity will double every year, and cost will drop by 20 to 30%.

Ted Hoff

In 1971, Marcian (Ted) Hoff, still fresh from postgraduate work at Stanford, conceived the microprocessor at Intel, and a talented Italian-born physicist, Federico Faggin, carried through with its development. Hoff's four-chip set, centered around one general-purpose logic device that would access its application instructions from semiconductor memory, replaced 12 custom chips in a programmable calculator—and could be adapted by programs to perform in many different applications. It packed as much computing power as the first electronic computer, the ENIAC, which filled a warehouse when it was built in 1946.

Xerox Corporation opened its Palo Alto Research Center in 1970. In ensuing years, PARC scientists developed a dozen groundbreaking computer technologies, some of them growing out of Douglas Englebart's original ideas at Stanford Research Institute. These included portable computing, the laser printer, the first easy-to-use word processing program, and desktop publishing's Postscript language. Other companies—notably Hewlett-Packard, Apple Computer, and Adobe Systems—later exploited most of these innovations.

1969
Apollo 11 lands on the moon with U.S. astronauts Neil Armstrong and Edwin Aldrin.

The world's first supersonic passenger aircraft, the Concorde, is created.

1970
Invention of the silicon chip in the U.S. marks a revolution in the electronics industry.

Northeastern Africa and southern Sahara experience severe droughts.

First cases appear of AIDS (Acquired Immune Deficiency Syndrome).

1972
Arab terrorists of "Black September" organization kill Israeli athletes disrupting the Munich Olympics.

Pong!

Semiconductor companies and production had zoomed so much that in 1971 Don Hoefler, editor of *Microelectronics News*, coined the name "Silicon Valley" as shorthand for the whole nexus of wondrous electronics products, instant millionaires, and brand-new industries. Hoefler also traced the history of semiconductor industry spinouts, pegging Fairchild as the most significant and adding, "Fairchild itself has spawned many firms, in instruments and production equipment as well as semiconductors."

More happenings made 1971 a milestone year. Stanford University and Stanford Research Institute cut their ties, the latter becoming independent as SRI International. Gene Amdahl, principal architect in Menlo Park of IBM's highly successful 360 mainframe series, left IBM to develop "plug-compatible manufacturing" at his own company. Also in 1971, Steve Wozniak went to work for Hewlett-Packard as a programmer. After Nolan Bushnell founded Atari in 1972 and began the computer games industry with a game called Pong, Wozniak's younger friend, Steve Jobs, joined Atari.

Although Pong thrived, consumer electronics—epitomized by the digital watch and the basic pocket calculator—enjoyed only a brief heyday in the United States before being crushed by Japanese competition, an event coinciding with the 1974-75 recession. Ampex was especially hard hit.

Biotechnology made one of its first big splashes in 1973 when Stanley N. Cohen of the Stanford medical school faculty and Herbert W. Boyer of the UC San Francisco medical school first demonstrated gene splicing. Patents on gene cloning and gene splicing became the two universities' big earners, with Genentech of South San Francisco a major developer.

Hewlett-Packard introduced the first programmable pocket calculator in 1974, co-opting the place of engineers' slide rules and starting HP in the computer business. In the same year, Siple Station in Antarctica was founded to study upper atmosphere physics in experiments headed by Robert Helliwell, Stanford electrical engineering professor.

At Stanford University, the Center for Integrated Systems took shape in 1974 to coordinate the combined forces of business, government, and higher education in the technology race. One of its codirectors was John Linvill, EE professor and inventor of telesensory processes such as the one enabling his blind daughter to read rapidly—and, in time, to earn a doctorate.

Kenneth Arrow, who had taught at Stanford from 1949 to 1968, and who later returned, was named co-winner of the 1972 Nobel Prize for Economics for his contributions to welfare economics and general economic equilibrium theory. Paul J. Flory of Stanford received the 1974 Nobel Prize for Chemistry for his investigations of synthetic and natural polymers, the macromolecules developed most notably in nylon and synthetic rubber.

Intel founders: Andy Grove, Bob Noyce, Gordon Moore

Watergate scandal breaks out when U.S. republican presidential aids bug Democratic headquarters.

1973
Arab and Israeli 'Yom-Kippur' War.

Oil crisis in the U.S. and Europe.

U.S. Supreme Court rule 7-2 in Roe v. Wade granting women the legal

option to abortion during the first trimester of pregnancy.

1974
President Richard Nixon resigns.

- 71 -

Chapter 12: Personal Computer Bursts Hobby Bonds

If you wanted an inexpensive microcomputer in 1975, you had one choice: Spend $498 on an Altair 8800 hobby kit, with Intel's third microprocessor, the 8080, at its heart. Once built, there was little you could do with it; still, the innovation excited techies. In March 1975, they formed the Homebrew Computer Club in Menlo Park, and soon drew turnouts so large they had to get permission to use SLAC's auditorium.

First Apple I

Steve Wozniak was a founding Homebrewer. When he saw the home computers others built, "Woz" felt he could do better. Buying a microprocessor cheap at a computer show, he built a machine around it, and at club meetings showed it and handed out copies of his design. The Apple I was an instant hit. His friend Steve Jobs suggested forming a company, and in 1976 Apple Computer started up in Jobs' Cupertino garage. Jobs, 20, and Wozniak, 25, moonlighted to fill orders until they could no longer meet the demand. Despite their pleas, their respective employers declined to adopt the product.

While Wozniak improved the design, Jobs sought backing. He was put in touch with A.C. (Mike) Markkula, 40, an Intel marketer then planning to retire early. Impressed by the Apple, Markkula persuaded the Steves to do a business plan, arranged financing, invested money of his own and stayed with the new company. In 1977 they introduced the Apple II, featuring a bold innovation, floppy-disk controllers, and Wozniak's simple but elegant design. Fully assembled (as Jobs sensed buyers wanted), it outstripped all projections, creating a PC market and sales topping $100 million by 1980.

On the large computer front, Tandem, a company started by James Treybig in 1974, worked on fault-tolerant computers. Amdahl, meanwhile, shipped its first plug-in compatible product in 1975. But the firm remained under heavy pressure due to underfinancing and IBM's rivalry. Gene Amdahl resigned in 1979; he later associated with Trilogy and Grid Systems. Another Amdahl employee, Lawrence Ellison, joined Robert Miner and Edward Oates in forming Oracle Systems in 1977 to create a relational database management system meeting theoretical specifications published by IBM.

Steven Wozniak

As for semiconductors, equipment vendors who founded the Semiconductor Equipment and Materials Institute in 1970 were having marked success. By 1975, their drive to set standards aimed at reducing waste, inventory and planning reached pay dirt. More than 80% of all new wafers met SEMI standards—a remarkable feat because Silicon Valley was approaching a 1980 census of close to 3,000 manufacturing companies. The manufacturers' group, the Western Electronics Manufacturing Association (WEMA),

1975
Japanese company JVC creates VHS (Video Home System).

1976
Zhou Enlai's and Mao Zedong's deaths put an end to the "Gang of Four."

1977
Earthquake in Tang Shan, China, kills 240,000.

1977
Astronauts observe rings around planet Uranus.

1978
Britain births the world's first 'test tube' baby.

1979
Margaret Thatcher is the first female prime minister of England.

James Treybig, founder Tandem

was renamed the American Electronics Association (AEA) in 1978. Intel marketed a microprocessor-based OEM (original equipment manufacturer) system in 1976—the first single-board computer. At National Semiconductor, Charles Sporck had honed manufacturing skills and made DRAMs (dynamic random access memories) a commodity product.

Silicon Valley scientists and engineers were puzzled by the emphasis Japanese companies were putting on CMOS (complementary metal oxide silicon) technology, which Fairchild had tried and discarded. Intel made limited use of CMOS in digital watches, but quit making them in 1979. CMOS was slow and drew relatively little power. The Japanese, with shrewd marketing eyes, saw its advantages in portable devices—watches, calculators, cameras, and TVs.

At Stanford University, the process of transferring faculty inventions to commercial firms to develop had taken shape in the Office of Technology Licensing. By 1980, OTL under Niels Reimers had helped professors patent more than 400 inventions, earning Stanford $61 million in royalties. The top money-earner proved to be music Professor John Chowning's FM synthesis. Chowning had discovered in 1967 that at a certain frequency, patterns of vibrations from two oscillators generated harmonic tones like those of musical instruments. Yamaha Corp. bought exclusive use of his 1977 patent, and in 1984 introduced its DX7 synthesizer, a must for rock bands and one of the most popular instruments ever.

NASA/Ames Research Center dedicated the Kuiper Airborne Observatory in 1975—a converted C-141 transport plane equipped with a 36-inch infrared telescope. In 1977, scientists aboard the Kuiper discovered that the planet Uranus possesses equatorial rings, composed of rock and ice. Later discoveries included Venus cloud composition, galactic center phenomena, star formation, and supernova mechanisms. In 1978, the Stanford-NASA Joint Institute for Surface and Microstructural Research formalized a collaboration begun in 1968. University departments of materials science, chemical engineering and electrical engineering were involved.

Three Stanford faculty superstars became Nobel laureates in the 1975-80 period. Burton Richter won the 1976 physics prize for his work at the Linear Accelerator Center in discovering the existence of the psi or J particle. Richter subsequently became SLAC's director. Milton Friedman won the 1976 economics prize for championing laissez-faire economics and, the next year, came to Stanford's Hoover Institution after 30 years at the University of Chicago. Paul Berg won the 1980 chemistry prize for his development of recombinant DNA techniques—work subsequently applied by a number of San Francisco Bay Area biotechnology companies.

Steven Jobs

1979
Somoza government undergoes civil war in Nicaragua; Sandinistas seize power.

Sony chairman Akio Morita of Japan invents portable stereo (the walkman).

Philips and Sony develop the compact disc.

Mobile or cellular telephone is invented in Sweden.

U.S. attempt to rescue hostages in Iran fails.

1980
U.S. space shuttle launched.

Since the release of its first innovative product, the Apple I computer, Cupertino, California-based Apple has been providing leading-edge electronic devices for creative professionals, developers, small businesses, scientists, educators, and consumers everywhere. But now, more than 30 years after its founding, the company is not only a premier computer developer, as its name change, from Apple Computer to Apple, reflects. The company is also a digital media powerhouse, providing best-selling portable music and video players as well as revolutionary mobile phones.

Steve Wozniak is shown here with the original Apple 1 board. The original Apple 1 was never put in a case, but sold as just the board.

It all began when "the two Steves," Apple co-founders Steve Wozniak and Steve Jobs, scrounged together the parts to build 50 "hobby computers" of their own design—pre-assembled computer circuit boards with no keyboard, case, sound, or graphics—for a local computer store called the Byte Shop. With money from the sale in hand, the two then quickly improved the design, with a better TV display interface, graphics, and a keyboard that made the computer ready to run. After joining with investor Mike Markkula and founding Apple Computer, in 1977 Jobs and Wozniak launched the Apple II, with the goal of changing the way people used information to work, learn, and play.

Early in 1977, Apple Computer moved from Steve Jobs' garage to rented space in the Stevens Creek Office Center, Cupertino, CA. Apple II made its debut there and the first Apple II was shipped four months later. This is a picture of Apple's new home.

Just a few years later, a group at Apple started to design a new computer that would ignite the personal computer revolution.

After studying Xerox PARC's research into the new GUI computer interface, Apple engineers developed the company's first GUI-based, rather than text-based, interface. The innovative Lisa computer had Apple's now-well-known windows and icons, but it was Apple's Macintosh line, which followed in 1984, that took a giant leap forward, making personal computing both user friendly and simple.

In 1991 Apple continued to build on its founders' guiding principle—that the individual, not the mainframe, should be at the center of the computing universe. The company introduced a

In 1976, as Apple orders increased, the business moved to larger quarters in the garage of the Jobs' home. By the end of 1976, Apple had done $100,000 in business on Apple I. It was during this period that Steve Wozniak completed his design of Apple II. This picture shows Steve Jobs at work in the garage — testing Apple I boards.

portable Mac, the Powerbook, which set the standard for the modern, ergonomic laptop, and in 1993 launched its first consumer device, the PDA called the Newton. In 1994 the company made available its Power Macintosh line, which incorporated IBM's high-performance PowerPC processor.

The end of the '90s saw yet another Apple breakthrough computer. The iMac provided not only power and ease of use, but its streamlined, translucent body reflected Apple's growing emphasis on design and aesthetics. The iMac, as well as the rest of the Mac line, now features such pluses as iLife software, for easily working with music, photos, and video; the capability to run all major operating systems; Apple's state-of-the-art Mac X operating system; security from viruses; and the latest Intel chips, all in a sleek, distinctive design.

Since the turn of the century, Apple has continued its innovative, successful streak. Apple Stores now dot the U.S., Asia, and Europe, providing the latest Apple products as well as customer support through the company's Genius Bars. The iPod portable digital music player is a smash hit with consumers, and Apple's newest consumer product, the revolutionary iPhone, which provides leading-edge phone, video, and Internet capabilities, is already sought after by consumers and professionals alike. Apple's history has been revolutionary, but its future promises to be as great.

In 1976, Apple's business was run from the garage in Steve Jobs' home.

A young Steve Jobs in 1976.

The KLA 100 was the first inspection product introduced by the company in 1978 to ensure the quality of photomasks.

KLA-Tencor Corporation is the world's leading supplier of process control and yield management solutions for the semiconductor and related microelectronics industries.

Headquartered in San Jose, Calif., with sales and support facilities around the world, the company has revenues of more than $2.7 billion. A J. P. Morgan analyst named KLA-Tencor one of the best-run semiconductor companies in the world.

KLA-Tencor's leadership resulted from the 1997 merger of two pioneering companies: KLA Instruments and Tencor Instruments. Founded in 1976 by current KLA-Tencor chairman Kenneth Levy and Robert Anderson, who met while at startup Computervision Corporation, KLA Instruments focused on improving the manufacturing yields for complex semiconductor devices. The company's first product, the KLA 100, which automatically inspected the photomasks that defined the pattern layers of integrated circuit fabrication, shipped in 1978. This innovative product reduced the time required for photomask inspection from eight hours to 15 minutes and provided a much more thorough inspection than previously could be done. In 1980 KLA broadened its product line to include wafer inspection and soon after expanded into wafer metrology as well as software that integrated inspection and measurement data for analysis.

Tencor Instruments also got its start in 1976 and introduced its first product just seven months later. The Alpha-Step significantly improved step height measurement, a process critical to producing precise semiconductor film layer thickness. Tencor's Surfscan product, which followed in 1984, raised the bar on particle and contamination detection based on laser-scanning technology. The company later expanded its offerings to include defect review and data analysis tools.

Today, the combined company is a new-product-introduction machine, introducing on average one new process control and yield management solution each month that spans a broad range of inspection and measurement requirements. A 2005 *Electronic Business* article focused on the company's product development and internal training programs while highlighting KLA-Tencor as one of Silicon Valley's most innovative companies. Leveraging KLA-Tencor's innovative solutions, semiconductor manufacturers are able to more quickly overcome the defect and parametric yield challenges that otherwise could cripple the performance, reliability, and affordability of new types of semiconductors. In addition the company's solutions help manufacturers get new products to market more quickly, thereby realizing greater revenues and profitability.

KLA-Tencor offers customers unmatched yield management and process control solutions that help them meet the challenges of increasing device complexity, reduced product life cycles, and increased competition. To continue to meet their customers' IC manufacturing challenges, KLA-Tencor is expanding its analysis software solutions. The company also created the industry's first yield management consulting practice to provide the systems, software, and experts needed to get customers' yield improvement programs quickly up and running. KLA-Tencor is committed to continuing to aggressively invest in new technologies and services to advance the excellence of process control and yield management.

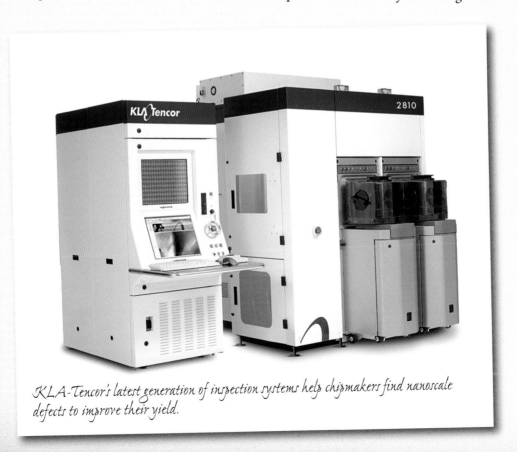

KLA-Tencor's latest generation of inspection systems help chipmakers find nanoscale defects to improve their yield.

Innovation is the force behind Oracle's success. Since co-founder and CEO Larry Ellison came across a research paper that described a working prototype for a relational database management system and discovered that no company had yet commercialized the technology, Oracle has continued to debut new products and functionality that advance database technology and applications that help customers access the information they need to respond quickly and effectively to market conditions.

It was in 1977 that Ellison, along with co-founders Bob Miner and Ed Oates, founded Software Development Labs (the company that would become Oracle). Just two years later, the trio released the first commercial SQL relational database management system, which defied the prevailing wisdom that technology would never scale to support large amounts of data or large numbers of users. The relational database software was a resounding success, and led to a revolution in enterprise computing.

Oracle then went on to develop many other successful firsts: the first database with read consistency, the first client-server database, the first UNIX-based accounting software, the first media server to support video on demand, the first Web database, the first database with XML support, and the first Internet development suite, among others. Through the expertise of top software engineers and feedback from its Fortune 500 customers, Oracle envisioned and created the products and functionality that information-driven businesses need.

Oracle's newest products, combined with its historical commitment to open standards and a comprehensive Internet strategy, continue to deliver both innovative technology and results. The turn of the millennium saw the release of Oracle E-Business Suite 11i,

CEO Lawrence J. Ellison

Oracle Headquarters

the industry's first integrated suite of enterprise applications. Oracle Real Application Clusters was then added to the Oracle9*i* Database, giving customers the option of running their IT on connected, low-cost servers. Oracle Database 10*g*, the first grid computing product available for the enterprise, debuted in 2003. And in 2006, the company announced its Oracle "Applications Unlimited" program, which helps ensure continued enhancements—and the benefits they bring to customers—to Oracle E-Business Suite and Oracle's JD Edwards, PeopleSoft, and Siebel product lines. The company's Oracle Fusion Middleware, a family of comprehensive, hot-pluggable middleware products that span process management, developer tools, and business intelligence, Oracle Fusion Applications, new architecture which will leverage a Service-Oriented Architecture and the services in Oracle Fusion Middleware, and the release of the latest version of its flagship product, Oracle Database 11g, position Oracle to continue to support and benefit its customers and drive the industry.

For 30 years, Oracle has been building on its thorough knowledge of customer challenges and on its ability to leverage both its great size and strength and the nimbleness of a much smaller company. From its tiny beginning it has grown into an industry-leading powerhouse that is the world's leading supplier of software for information management as well as the world's second-largest independent software company. Oracle technology can be found in nearly every industry and in the data centers of 98 of the Fortune 100 companies. The company's goal is to become the leader in middleware as well as in applications and to continue focusing on solving its customers' information-management problems.

IBM 5050 Personal Computer

In 1981, International Business Machines Corp. entered the personal computer market, and was welcomed as a competitor, rather slyly, by Apple. IBM's PC boasted a disk operating system that became an industry standard. Hewlett-Packard had launched its first PC in 1980. The early '80s were to be dominated by microcomputer expansions—and by a torrid pace of start-ups.

Steadily improving microprocessors triggered a related explosion of other peripherals: printers, modems, disk drives, interlinked networks, equipment for building chips, video games, computer-assisted design. The games business reached its zenith in 1981 and by 1983 was plummeting.

The race to gain share in the expanding PC market created a profusion of new models, some of them tardy though much ballyhooed — a phenomenon scornfully called "vaporware." In 1983, IBM introduced its PC-XT, the first personal computer with a built-in (10-megabit) hard drive. Meanwhile, Compaq marketed a "clone" of an IBM PC, starting production of a flood of IBM compatibles by rivals trying to improve on and/or undersell the industry standard-bearer.

Apple offered an expensive model called the Lisa in 1983, and it flopped. Recovering in 1984, Apple introduced the Macintosh to instant popularity. The Mac made affordable innovations that had been part of the Lisa, such as pull-down menus and the mouse as an alternative to moving the cursor with keystrokes. The Mac's special graphics capabilities endeared it to illustrators and designers.

Computer-assisted design (CAD) took off after invention of the silicon compiler in 1979. Former Stanford professor James N. Clark founded Silicon Graphics in 1982 to develop three-dimensional computer graphics and marketed the first 3-D work station in 1984. Edward McCracken later replaced Clark as Silicon Graphics CEO.

Another 1982 start-up was Sun Microsystems, also born in a Stanford laboratory. Sun founders Andreas Bechtolsheim, Scott McNealy, and Vinod Khosla, abetted by Stanford professor Forest Baskett, saw potential for workstations able to share data using the UNIX operating system favored by scientists and engineers. McNealy became the CEO.

Daisywheel and dot-matrix printers, the early choices, began to give way in 1984 when Hewlett-Packard pioneered inkjet technology.

John Warnock and Charles Geschke led a group of former Xerox PARC scientists in founding Adobe Systems in 1982. They aimed to

Scott McNealy, 1985.

1981	1982		1983		
Egyptian president Anwar Sadat is assassinated.	Israeli forces invade southern Lebanon; massacre of Palestinians in Beirut refugee camp.	War between Argentina and Britain (Falklands War).	Conflict in Sudan; more than 1.5 million people died.	Sally Ride blasts off on six-day Challenger flight.	U.S.S.R. shoots down Korean Air Lines passenger plane.

- 80 -

develop a standard computer language that would consistently transmit even the most complex pages to a printer. Their scalable-font software product, PostScript, eventually became the industry standard.

Another 1982 start-up, Cypress Semiconductor, began when a group of CMOS (complementary metal oxide semiconductor) engineers led by T.J. Rodgers deemed Advanced Micro Devices too slow to adopt that technology and programmable gate arrays. CMOS, as the Japanese had learned, proved to be a "slow and low" (low-powered) answer for small battery-driven electronic devices such as notebook computers, and Cypress found a niche at the high end of the customized chip market.

Xilinx entered the customizing arena in 1984 to create field-programmable gate arrays, enabling buyers to customize computer instructions to fit their own needs. Bernie Vonderschmitt, Ross Freeman, and Jim Barnett, former Zilog employees, were its founders.

John Warnock

Another 1984 start-up was Cisco Systems, founded by a husband-and-wife team, Leonard Bosack and Sandra Lerner. Cisco used technology Bosack had developed to link Stanford computers so he and his bride-to-be could communicate, though in separate departments. Later in the '80s, when the market for network routers opened up, Cisco was ready.

Cirrus Logic also made its debut in 1984, adapting an efficient chip developed by Suhas Patil to the first controllers built directly on a disk drive. This led to the PC industry's shift to smaller disk drives. Sybase Inc. entered the high-performance relational database management field in 1984 in competition with Oracle Systems and became a significant player in the 1990s.

Space shuttle Columbia

Although U.S. firms had controlled the semiconductor memory market throughout the 1970s, 1984 brought a startling reversal as Japanese producers moved into an early lead and went on to capture all of the 256K DRAM market, thus dominating the latest development. Wails that Silicon Valley had lost its edge began to make headlines.

Stanford professor Henry Taube won the 1983 Nobel Prize for Chemistry for new discoveries in the basic mechanism of chemical reactions. One application of his findings has been in selecting metallic compounds for use as superconductors.

The U.S. space shuttle grabbed the manned-flight spotlight, with Columbia beginning operational missions late in 1982. Challenger first flew in 1983, Discovery in 1984.

1984

Sikhs assassinate Indira Gandhi, Indian prime minister.

New Zealand declared a nuclear-free zone.

Failure of rain dependent crops after extensive drought causing famine in Africa.

First acknowledgment of famine in Ethiopia, Sudan, and Chad by the - 81 west.

Attempt by the IRA to assassinate British cabinet.

Headquartered in Fremont, Lam Research Corporation is a major provider of wafer fabrication equipment and services to the worldwide semiconductor industry.

t Fremont, California–based Lam Research Corporation, company success is based on company values: honesty and integrity, achievement, mutual trust and respect, open communication, ownership and accountability, teamwork, and putting the customer first—before the company and the employee. And success has been achieved—Lam's core values have enabled the major supplier of manufacturing equipment for the global semiconductor industry to become not only one of the world's leading high tech companies, according to *BusinessWeek*, but one of the best places to work in the Bay Area, according to three business journals.

More than 25 years ago, Lam Research was founded by David Lam, an MIT graduate who tackled semiconductor etch technology head on. Etch processing tools and technology became the foundation of the company, with the initial product a plasma-etching system for manufacturing chips. By 1983 the company was successfully selling a state-of-the-art silicon etch system, and in 1984, shortly after Lam had its initial public offering, Dr. Lam left the company to pursue computer software development.

At the time, rapidly increasing chip demand was driven by new generations of PCs and the "next best electronic gadgets," such as multi-functional cell phones and game systems, all of which required smaller and higher-density chips. Despite increased competition from chip-manufacturing system suppliers and the industry's cyclical ups and downs, Lam Research thrived by delivering technology breakthroughs that enabled leading semiconductor manufacturers to meet their technology goals, and that eventually gave Lam the number one etch market share position, which it has held since 2000.

In 1997 Lam acquired OnTrak Systems, a chip equipment manufacturer that specialized in equipment for cleaning silicon wafers. OnTrak also supplied Lam with a new and dynamic president and CEO, James Bagley, now executive chairman of the board. The same year also brought current president and

Stephen G. Newberry, president and CEO, Lam Research Corporation.

James W. Bagley, executive chairman of the board of directors, Lam Research Corporation.

CEO Steve Newberry to the technology powerhouse. Bagley and Newberry, former colleagues at Applied Materials, teamed up to rebuild Lam with a values-based culture, created from their own winning behaviors and strong values.

The two men consolidated operations and left the CVD business. They also set out to make Lam number one in customer trust—"Not customer satisfaction," as Newberry said, "but trust." They leveraged their intimate knowledge of the industry and customer needs and opened a world-class R&D facility staffed by results-driven people, thereby linking business success to customer results. The company invested heavily in R&D and won numerous customer and industry awards for its advanced technology offerings and excellent customer satisfaction.

Over the past decade, Bagley and Newberry have made good on their goals to lead Lam to new heights. They continue to lead their market with new products that address chip manufacturing challenges as the industry moves into advanced technology nodes. By providing major device manufacturers such as Sony, Samsung, and IBM with state-of-the-art technology and systems, Lam is well positioned for further growth.

And by focusing Lam's resources on its core competencies—product development, sales and marketing, and customer service—and restructuring the company to succeed, Bagley and Newberry have created an organization that not only sees record profits and is recognized for the way it does business but provides trusted solutions to satisfied customers.

Lam's 2300® Exelan® Flex45™ Etch System

ince its founding in 1981 by Executive Chairman Robert Swanson, Vice President of Engineering and Chief Technical Officer Robert Dobkin, and three other leading engineers, Linear Technology has been focused on only one thing: designing and manufacturing the industry's highest performance linear, or analog, integrated circuits. That singular focus turned a belief into a success. Linear has joined the S&P 500 index of major public companies and was ranked in 2007 as the most profitable semiconductor company in Silicon Valley.

How does a company that produces analog products reign supreme in a global market hungering for more and more advanced digital devices? The answer is that digital circuits process the information in the form of on-off electrical signals involved in computational functions. Analog circuits monitor, condition, and transform real-world signals associated with temperature, pressure, weight, position, light, sound, and speed—in other words, analog circuits act as a bridge between the digital world and the real world.

While some thought the advent of the Digital Age signaled the demise of the analog chip, Robert Swanson and Robert Dobkin knew better. Though today's feature-rich cell phones, computers, and other multimedia devices hadn't yet been envisioned when they left National Semiconductor to found Linear Technology, they were certain analog chips would continue to play a crucial role in electronic products for precise control and power management. Since the early 1980s, other semiconductor companies have plowed resources into expensive digital development while Swanson kept Linear focused on developing analog chips, a market projected to reach $40 billion by 2008.

According to CEO Lothar Maier, Linear's analog circuits now play a crucial role in diverse electronic products from over 15,000 customers, including cell phones, notebook and desktop computers, video and multimedia players, industrial instrumentation, automotive electronics, factory automation, network infrastructure, and military and space systems. Linear manufacturers and ships 7,500 different products that continue to meet the needs of high-end electronic product innovators and their tech-hungry customers.

Linear Technology CEO Lothar Maier and Founder and Executive Chairman Bob Swanson have led the company through the $1 billion mark.

Linear outperforms its competitors with superior design innovation and world-class, high-reliability production, regularly rolling out groundbreaking products—close to 200 a year. Its engineers design feature-rich circuits responsible for major new product innovations. For example, Linear engineers designed special analog circuits for Apple's revolutionary iPod music player. Linear's top-flight designers, located in 12 design centers throughout the world, along with its technical sales force and field applications engineers, have enabled the company to penetrate diverse global markets and surpass $1 billion in sales.

Groundbreaking for the second Linear Technology building in 1986. Pictured from the right are Brian Hollins, Robert Swanson, Robert Dobkin and the builder.

The company's leading-edge manufacturing facilities have also played a key role in its success. In 1982 Linear opened its first wafer fabrication plant in California. The company now employs over 3,800, has manufacturing and test facilities in California, Washington, Singapore, and Malaysia, and uses its own state-of-the-art process technologies to produce the industry's highest quality circuits.

Since its beginnings over 25 years ago, Linear has supplied high-performance analog chips for an increasing array of applications. As the demand for faster and more feature-rich digital products grows, Linear will continue to serve its customers with focused analog innovation and excellence.

Linear Technology engineers examine the design of an analog integrated circuit. From the left, George Erdi, Robert Dobkin, Bob Widlar, Carl Nelson, and Tom Redfern.

In 1981, Stanford University engineering professor Dr. John Hennessy, along with his team, began work on a microprocessor architecture that would dramatically increase performance in a broad range of computer-based devices. Today, the MIPS® architecture is #1 in many of the fastest growing embedded markets for digital consumer and business applications, including cable modems, set-top boxes, DVD recorders, DSL, digital TVs, wired and wireless Networking, VoIP, and the backbone of the Internet.

In his quest for higher performance, Hennessy took a new approach to deep instruction pipelining, a processing technique that spread the running of an instruction into several steps, basically causing the instruction to pause until all steps were completed and preventing additional data from being loaded. Though the process was well known at the time, the "interlocks" were thought to be a major barrier to speed improvements. So Hennessy and his group designed a microprocessor that enabled instructions to complete in only one cycle, eliminating the need for interlocks and increasing performance. They named their processor MIPS, for microprocessor without interlocked pipeline stages.

The new design, however, was not without controversy. It eliminated a number of useful instructions, such as multiply and divide, that need multiple steps to complete. Many in the industry believed that replacing complex multiple instructions with many simpler additions would not increase speed.

But Hennessy was certain that the new design had enormous performance potential; he knew speed was in the pipelines, not in the instructions. In 1984 he left Stanford and co-founded MIPS Computer Systems with fellow researchers Dr. John Moussouris and Robert Wall, to design and deliver MIPS microprocessors.

Hennessy took the lead in creating streamlined processors with a scalability that would meet the demands of generations of wide-ranging applications. By 1991 the company's R4000 processor, the first 64-bit microprocessor, was named "Microprocessor of the Year" by

MIPS32® 34K™ Family

MIPS32® 24K® Family

Microprocessor Report. By 1996 the MIPS architecture had become the highest-volume, fastest-growing RISC architecture in the world.

After going public in 1989, MIPS was acquired by Silicon Graphics in 1992 to ensure the availability of future generations of its high-performance 64-bit processors. The company, renamed MIPS Technologies, operated as a wholly owned subsidiary of SGI until the late 1990s, when the highly successful group was spun off to develop and license its intellectual property: 32- and 64-bit MIPS architectures and microprocessor cores. In 1998 the company made an initial public offering as MIPS Technologies, Inc., and by the start of the new century, headed by President and CEO John Bourgoin, was a leader in the embedded processor industry.

Today, MIPS is the second largest processor IP company worldwide. MIPS Technologies and its licensees provide the broadest range of 32- and 64-bit processors and cores for the most advanced digital products and the networks that connect them. As the company looks to the future, it will continue to provide open, licensable architecture for maximum design flexibility; rapid, reliable, cost-effective development supported by hundreds of tools and the most popular operating systems; seamless 32- and 64-bit compatibility to protect software investments; and solutions that provide the highest performance and lowest power solutions.

Adobe Systems and the Information Age have been perfect partners for more than 25 years. Since 1982 Adobe has been delivering award-winning software and technologies that have redefined and advanced business and personal communications.

Based in San Jose, Calif., Adobe is one of the largest and most diversified software companies in the world. Its cutting-edge solutions are used in every corner of the globe and in nearly every industry, from publishing to government to financial services to education to telecommunications. Customers include industry leaders such as Nokia, Yahoo!, Deutsche Bank, Hearst Magazines, and Wal-Mart and major governmental agencies such as the U.S. Internal Revenue Service. Adobe also works with an extensive network of solution providers who develop customized applications that meet a wide range of business needs.

John Warnock – Founder

Chuck Geschke – Founder

Finding a solution to the problem of accurately translating text and images from a computer screen to print was what drove Adobe's founders to start their own company. In the late 1970s, John Warnock and Chuck Geschke met at the renowned Xerox Palo Alto Research Center (PARC) where they researched device-independent graphic systems and printing. When they realized that their work could revolutionize computing, they left the lab and together founded Adobe—named after the creek that ran behind Warnock's home in Los Altos, Calif.—and developed a radical new way to print text and images on paper. Their first product, PostScript®, which incorporates a page-description language that enables a computer file to be printed exactly as it appears on the screen, is still the industry standard and now allows digital printing on corporate networks, the Internet and digital document distribution systems.

From their early success, the two men quickly expanded their focus to desktop software applications, helping ignite the desktop publishing revolution. Adobe Illustrator® and Adobe Photoshop® were groundbreaking software that redefined the quality and complexity of images that could be created for print, and now, in later versions, extends those benefits to video, film, and the Web. More than 90% of creative professionals worldwide have Photoshop software, for digital image editing and creation, on their desktops.

The 1990s saw more exciting additions to Adobe's line of powerful, creative solutions. Adobe Premiere and Adobe After Effects became essential tools for motion graphics, visual effects and digital video editing. In 1996 Adobe Flash®—which today is installed on nearly 98% of all Internet-connected desktops—began providing the

Adobe® Acrobat® 8 Professional

most advanced way to create interactive Websites, interact with digital games and entertainment, and drive mobile content. In 1997 Adobe Dreamweaver became the must-have application for designing, developing, and maintaining Websites. And in 1999 Adobe launched InDesign®, professional layout and design software that provides sophisticated graphics and typography.

Furthering the founders' vision of reinventing and improving computing, the company introduced software in 1993 it called Adobe Acrobat. Acrobat revolutionized information sharing by enabling people

Adobe Creative Suite® 3 Design Premium

around the world to deliver and receive digital documents exactly as they were meant to be—just as PostScript exactly translated computer text and images to paper. With Acrobat the Portable Digital Format, or PDF, became—and still is—the de facto standard for sharing digital documents. Today more than 250,000,000 PDF files exist on the Web and the world's top-10 PC manufacturers ship their systems with PDF technology installed. The new century saw the introduction of groundbreaking products for developers and the enterprise as well as for mobile applications. Launched in 2003, Adobe Flex™ gave the enterprise a powerful set of building blocks for creating a richer, more responsive presentation tier for enterprise applications. Adobe's LiveCycle® family, introduced in 2004, enables enterprises to automate and simplify the flow of information and secures business processes beyond the firewall. Adobe Flash Lite and FlashCast meet increasing consumer demand for compelling, easy-to-use mobile data services and Adobe Reader®LE enables mobile devices to interact easily and reliably with PDF files. Adobe Reader and Flash Player software combined can be found on over 700,000,000 connected PCs and devices worldwide.

The start of the new millennium also saw a change in Adobe leadership. In 2000 Chuck Geschke retired, followed by John Warnock in 2001. Current CEO Bruce Chizen continues to focus on the company's mission of revolutionizing how the world engages with ideas and information. During his tenure, Chizen has strengthened Adobe's position as a platform provider for software users and developers across a variety of markets. He has also nurtured the kind of company culture that has brought Adobe accolades, including being named eight times to *FORTUNE* magazine's "Best Places to Work For" list.

Adobe has established itself as an engaged and responsible corporate citizen worldwide, working to make the places where its employees live and work better, stronger and more vibrant. The company offers cash grants and in-kind contributions, including donated software, volunteer support, and software training, to non-profit organizations. In 2006 Adobe launched a signature philanthropy program, Adobe Youth Voices, aimed at helping young people everywhere acquire valuable technology skills while developing deeper connections with their communities. The company is also a leader in promoting environmental stewardship and creating healthy work environments. In December 2006, Adobe became the world's first commercial enterprise to receive three Platinum certifications from the U.S. Green Building Council (USGBC), under the Leadership in Energy and Environmental Design (LEED®)-Existing Building Program for its facilities in

Bruce Chizen – CEO

San Jose. LEED certification of Adobe's other U.S. facilities is underway, and a similar set of environmental standards is being applied to Adobe's operations around the world.

Adobe's commitment to revolutionizing how people engage with ideas and information is as strong today as it was in 1982. Nearly all text and images seen in magazines, on billboards, and in advertisements—or experienced in movies and on television screens and digital devices—has been touched by Adobe software. With its focus on innovation, Adobe continues to reinvent how the world creates, perceives, and engages with information.

Adobe headquarters

The value behind E*TRADE FINANCIAL lies in its tireless effort to challenge the old ways of doing business. The company succeeds in delivering an integrated portfolio of innovative, customer-focused brokerage and banking products and services by remaining true to its operating ideals and well-proven formula – regularly asking, "Can this be done

San Francisco Market Street facilities

better?" By applying this level of discipline to the retail and institutional businesses, E*TRADE FINANCIAL is delivering long-term value to its customers and shareholders.

Mitchell Caplan
CEO of E*TRADE
Financial Corporation

E*TRADE FINANCIAL is also the only true global franchise in its category, with operations in the Americas, Europe, the Middle East, and Asia. The Company's global presence includes U.S. based headquarters, 11 additional physical locations and branded websites in 17 countries.

Key Company Milestones for this industry pioneer include:

- 1982: Bill Porter, an acclaimed physicist, inventor, and entrepreneur, developed leading-edge back-end technology that enabled the first online trade, made by a doctor in Michigan.

- 1992: E*TRADE expanded from Wall Street to Main Street, offering online trading services directly to individual investors through several online services. Just four years later, the etrade.com website was launched, and E*TRADE Group went public.

- 1996: E*TRADE launched the etrade.com website and shares of the company went public.

- 2000: E*TRADE was one of the first online companies to take advantage of the 1999 repeal of the Depression-era Glass-Steagel Act and began incorporating a bank to provide customers with an integrated way to manage their complete financial portfolios.

- 2005: the company began offering customers its Digital Security ID, a two-factor authentication device that thwarts would-be thieves from stealing an online customer's identity—an industry first for U.S. retail customers. That same year saw the launch of E*TRADE Complete, an intelligent, integrated way for customers to manage all of their money.

- In 2006 E*TRADE began providing its Complete Protection Guarantee – The industry's first fraud coverage and payment protection for the retail consumer, employing strict physical, electronic, and procedural safeguards designed to protect its customers' non-public information. The guarantee covers any loss that results from the unauthorized use of a customer's brokerage, banking or lending services.

- In 2007 the company launched its Global Trading platform, a service that provides online access to foreign stocks and currencies in six international markets, giving customers the ability to buy, hold, and sell in each market's local currency.

Jarrett Lilien
President and COO of
*E*TRADE Financial*
Corporation

Company Leadership:

- Mitchell H. Caplan, Chief Executive Officer and Director
- R. Jarrett Lilien, President, Chief Operating Officer and Director
- Connie M. Dotson, Chief Communications Officer
- Arlen W. Gelbard, Chief Administrative Officer and General Counsel, E*TRADE FINANCIAL; President, E*TRADE Bank
- Robert J. Simmons, Chief Financial Officer
- Nicholas A. Utton, Chief Marketing Officer
- Dennis J. Webb, President, E*TRADE Capital Markets

With its highly experienced management team leading the way – E*TRADE FINANCIAL continues to bring value to customers and shareholders, building on the company's history of strength, stability, value, ease of use and service.

E-Trade Signage

Since its launch in 1982, Sun Microsystems has pursued the radical vision that inspired its four young founders: to connect everyone and everything through technology innovation and sharing. Working to realize that vision has resulted in Sun's position as a leading global supplier of network computing solutions that power the world's most important markets.

Sun's four founders in 1982 — Vinod Khosla, Bill Joy, Andy Bechtolsheim, and Scott McNealy.

Sun's founding was based on a need. In 1981, Stanford University graduate student Andreas (Andy) Bechtolsheim became frustrated with continually having to trek to the campus computer center whenever his work required a powerful system. So, using readily available and inexpensive parts, Bechtolsheim built a high-performance workstation for himself, a system based on an "open" design that ran the powerful yet complex UNIX® OS. He called his creation Sun, short for Stanford University Network.

Word of Bechtolsheim's work spread and attracted the interest of Stanford MBA graduate Vinod Khosla. Khosla, a founder of CAE pioneer Daisy, felt that the industry needed a general-purpose workstation and that Bechtolsheim's design had huge potential. Khosla convinced Bechtolsheim to join him in building a company to produce one.

Scott McNealy — Sun's Chairman of the Board and CEO for 22 years.

With Khosla's business acumen and Bechtolsheim's systems expertise, the next step was to find a software guru, and with Bill Joy they found just that. As the principal architect and designer for UC Berkeley's UNIX, Joy was already widely known for his work and was the clear choice to head the new company's software efforts.

The final cornerstone of the founding team was Scott McNealy, another Stanford MBA, to run manufacturing. McNealy, the son of an American

Motors executive, immediately saw the promise of Sun as well as the opportunity to dramatically change the fundamentals of the computer industry.

Together, the four founders embarked on a mission that continues today: to defy conventional thinking, to succeed through creativity and innovation, to develop open technologies and products that solve the world's biggest business problems, and to have fun along the way.

Just three months after its launch, Sun began manufacturing and shipping its first computers, most of which the cofounders and a few employees assembled by hand. The Sun-1™ workstation, which included both BSD UNIX and TCP/IP standard, and the follow-on Sun-2™ workstation were immediate successes, helping the young company achieve $8 million in sales its first year.

While revenue initially came primarily from the university sector, Sun quickly began targeting new markets and soon found itself in the mainstream technical arena. In fact, Sun began growing at one of the most impressive rates ever — after just six years, Sun revenues had reached $1 billion, the fastest rise ever for a computer company with a direct sales force. Yet even as the company became a major force in the industry, with Scott McNealy at the helm it continued to foster its unique corporate culture: Work hard. Play hard. Stay ahead of the competition by changing the rules. And WIN!

For the first five years, Sun systems were based on Motorola 680x0 processors. But in 1987, all that changed. Sun saw the potential of reduced instruction set computing (RISC) in 1985 and set out to develop a new architecture based on that approach. Just two years later, Sun unveiled its first system based on its new SPARC® architecture. Coincidentally, Sun also became the leader in the workstation market that same year.

In 1989, Sun introduced the SPARCstation™ 1 workstation, a small, inexpensive desktop system that fit into a 3"x16"x16" enclosure, aptly named the "pizza box." The new system enabled Sun to take another giant leap, this time into the enormous commercial marketplace. Proving that it was a true systems company — offering both hardware and software — in 1991 Sun announced its new Solaris™ Operating System, the industry's first shrink-wrapped distributed computing environment.

The early 1990s saw other visible signs of success. In 1992, the company's name appeared on the Standard & Poor's 500. In 1993, Sun made its debut on the Fortune 500. That same year, Sun reached another incredible milestone — one million systems shipped in just over 10 years. As Scott McNealy said, "You need to be a big company to afford the investments in next-generation technologies." And by 1993, Sun had definitely become one of *the* big companies.

During the early '90s, something more important than anyone could have ever imagined was also beginning to take

Sun's current corporate headquarters at the Agnews Historic Park in Santa Clara, CA.

*James Gosling,
the father of Java.*

"It became obvious that Java technology and the Internet were made for each other. Our early demos brought animated objects and dynamic content to life within browser windows for the first time."

—James Gosling

form. Several Sun engineers worked quietly in an unmarked office to develop a hardware-independent platform that they planned to use to gain a foothold in the digital cable business. The technology they came up with — the breakthrough universal software called Java™ — was ahead of its time for the cable industry. But in 1995 it was perfect for the Internet, which was poised for explosive growth. In the words of James Gosling, the "father of Java," "It became obvious that Java technology and the Internet were made for each other. Our early demos brought animated objects and dynamic content to life within browser windows for the first time."

The introduction of Java technology in 1995 wasn't a typical product announcement. When Scott McNealy detailed the new technology at the SunWorld™ Conference, the crowd's enthusiastic reaction was greater than expected. Then came more. Netscape announced that its next version of the Navigator™ browser would include embedded Java technology. Not formally available yet, Java already had a major endorsement. Later that year, Microsoft announced its intent to include Java technology in its Internet Explorer browser. With the industry's two main browsers supporting the new technology, a landslide of companies — from Apple to HP to IBM — wanted to license Java technology.

A year after Java was up and running, Sun made it available worldwide by licensing the technology to all major hardware and software companies. Over the next few years, an enormous number of improvements and applications resulted from Java technology efforts around the world. In order to evaluate and coordinate these efforts, Sun created the Java Community Process℠, an open, all-inclusive community — that today numbers more than 1120 members — designed to help shape the direction of the Java platform.

As Java technology became more and more widespread, it was no longer considered just a rough language. Java technology had become refined and sophisticated, and in 1999 Sun announced three Java platforms targeted at the three key areas of networking: the desktop, the enterprise, and mobile devices.

Java is considered one of the greatest technology achievements ever, as well as one of the most widely used. In just over 10 years, Java has become the world's #1 programming platform. Today, there are more than five million developers, architects, and programmers creating the next generation of applications. Java is used in every major industry segment worldwide. With its versatility, efficiency, platform portability, and security, Java technology powers more than 5.5 billion devices, including more than 800 million PCs, 1.8 billion mobile phones and other handheld devices, 3 billion smart cards, and 11 million set-top boxes, printers, games, and more.

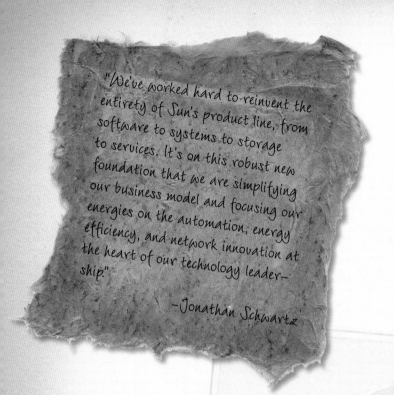

"We've worked hard to reinvent the entirety of Sun's product line, from software to systems to storage to services. It's on this robust new foundation that we are simplifying our business model and focusing our energies on the automation, energy efficiency, and network innovation at the heart of our technology leadership."

—Jonathan Schwartz

"What started out as just a programming language has exploded into a ubiquitous technology platform that today touches the lives of people all over the planet, in virtually every industry," says Sun President and CEO Jonathan Schwartz. "Java technology connects enterprises with their employees, partners, and customers. It's used in industries from retail and commerce to science and medicine. It helps governments deliver critical services to their citizenry and make lives better. And it powers the widest range of technology, from smart cards and mobile phones to the largest multiprocessor computers."

While Sun devoted much time and effort to helping Java technology grow, it was also busy expanding in other areas. In 1996, Sun unveiled its next-generation SPARC architecture, the UltraSPARC® processor. This new 64-bit processor became the basis of a new family of graphics workstations and a broad range of scalable, binary-compatible servers. In 1998, Sun introduced a new 64-bit version of its successful Solaris Operating System to accompany its 64-bit systems. The new OS delivered dramatic increases in performance, capacity, and scalability. And in 1999, Sun announced its new Sun Ray™ ultra-thin clients. These stateless, diskless desktops provided an interoperable desktop solution that dramatically reduced maintenance, upgrade, and operational costs. Through their revolutionary hot-desking technology, users could virtually take their desktop with them.

With the advent of the new millennium, Sun began its quest to remove the complexities of computing, treating computing like a service. In 2002, Sun introduced N1™, the first architecture to treat the network as a computer. By reducing the complexity associated with managing individual components, N1 technology helped businesses manage their environments as though they were single systems. In 2003, the Sun Java Enterprise System signaled a revolution in the software industry with its subscription-based approach to infrastructure software that dramatically simplified the acquisition, deployment, and maintenance of enterprise infrastructure software. Also that year, Sun announced a partnership with AMD to deliver powerful, low-cost 64-bit systems based on the x86 architecture. And in 2004, Sun unveiled the Solaris 10 OS for UltraSPARC, x64, and x86 systems. This latest version offered many new groundbreaking features, making it the most advanced — and the #1 — UNIX operating system on the planet.

In 2005 and 2006, Sun delivered one milestone after another. It open-sourced the code to its highly

The fab four reunite in 2006 — 24 years of incredible technological innovations.

popular and successful Solaris 10 OS. With the acquisition of StorageTek, the company offered the industry's broadest portfolio of storage and data management solutions. New Sun Fire™ x64 servers, the result of Sun's partnership with AMD, set new standards for performance and power efficiency while providing the flexibility to run multiple operating systems: Solaris, Linux, or Windows. Sun also announced new Sun Fire systems based on its UltraSPARC T1 processor with CoolThreads™ technology, the industry's first multithreaded processor designed for eco responsibility. With the high-performance, energy-efficient UltraSPARC T1 processor, these servers set new standards in performance as well as power and space efficiency, and addressed the skyrocketing energy costs in the datacenter. In addition to its new CoolThreads servers, Sun also introduced Project Blackbox, the first totally virtualized, modular datacenter built in a standard 20-foot shipping container. Optimized to deliver extreme energy, space, and performance efficiencies, Project Blackbox highlighted Sun's leadership in the green-computing movement. And with Sun Grid, Sun enabled customers to purchase computing and storage power as they need it, without the long-term costs of capital ownership, management, support, and real estate.

For Sun, 2007 was another year of key innovations. In technology, they introduced the UltraSPARC T2 — the next-generation processor with CoolThreads technology. Providing 8 cores, and 8 threads per core, for a total of 64 threads, the T2 increases capacity and performance and integrates networking and security features — all while maintaining a commitment to energy efficiency. In alliances, Sun announced a partnership with Intel to deliver x64 systems. This collaboration broadened Sun's offering in the x64 market with processors from the industry's two key providers. And in its continuing commitment to sharing, Sun released its highly acclaimed Java technology to the free and open source community. This represented one of the largest source code contributions and open source releases of one of the industry's most significant and pervasive technologies — and made Sun the #1 contributor to open source.

Today, Sun's vision of an open source community is as relevant as it was more than 25 years ago. Its open source approach can be found throughout its product line as well as its history, from the NFS file system in 1984 to Java technology-based developer tools, from its flagship Solaris OS to its new record-setting UltraSPARC T1 processor. Sun's beliefs in openness and sharing have been instrumental in its ability to create and deliver solutions that help customers be successful.

Sun's President and CEO Jonathan Schwartz.

To support its mission, Sun invests heavily in R&D to develop and deliver superior solutions. At times, it also acquires other great complementary technologies, such as those developed by Kealia, SeeBeyond, StorageTek, and others, to extend and enhance its own leading-edge technology and deliver even better solutions to its forward-thinking customers. The company also believes that partnering is a key to success. That's why it collaborates with leading industry innovators in creating and sharing technology, and works closely with ISVs, OEMs, service and system providers, and channel partners.

More than a quarter century ago, Sun was founded with one driving vision: The Network is the Computer™. Throughout the years, Sun has pioneered ideas such as open standards, interoperability, and open communities, and consistently broken through the barriers of conventional thinking to deliver innovative technologies. Sun has shared its ideas, expertise, and technology in order to eliminate the obstacles to access and help people to interact, share, and create new opportunities via the network.

Delivering technologies and products that power everything from mobile phones and smart cards to supercomputers and the Internet has clearly kept Sun at the forefront of the technology industry. And so has its leadership in the area of eco responsibility. In addition to continually reexamining its business and practices to operate as efficiently as possible, Sun also delivers entire technology ecosystems that provide more performance, take up less space, and use less energy.

Sun's vision that The Network is the Computer has never been more true than today. It remains at the core of everything Sun does. Going forward, Sun will continue to deliver more and more increasingly valuable products and services. And, as always, Sun will remain laser-focused on providing superior choice, innovation, and value to its customers.

"Momentum is clearly increasing around Sun, with Java, Solaris, Sun Fire, and StorageTek™ platforms all gaining share," says Jonathan Schwartz. "We've worked hard to reinvent the entirety of Sun's product line, from software to systems to storage to services. It's on this robust new foundation that we are simplifying our business model and focusing our energies on the automation, energy efficiency, and network innovation at the heart of our technology leadership."

Founded in 1982 by computer scientist Gary Hendrix, Symantec was a spin-off of Machine Intelligence, a start-up company formed by artificial intelligence researchers from SRI and Stanford University. In 1984, before the company even completed its first product, Symantec was acquired by another small start-up firm, C&E Software, run by Denis Coleman and Gordon Eubanks. The two leaders decided to retain the name Symantec and Eubanks served as CEO until 1999.

Symantec's first successful product was the award-winning database product Q&A, which used natural language processing to enable users to make queries in an English-like language. In the 1980s and 1990s, the company evolved into the software publishing business, adding to its product line by acquiring several companies. The most important of these acquisitions was Peter Norton Computing, the maker of a well-regarded utility program for PCs. By the late 1990s, Symantec marketed three major product lines: security and assurance (Norton AntiVirus and Norton Utilities), remote productivity solutions (WinFax PRO, pcAnywhere, and ACT!), and Internet tools (Symantec Café and Visual Café).

1988 Q&A Database Product

Dr. Gary Hendrix, founder of Symantec, 1982

The security business got its start with the release of the SAM product—Symantec AntiVirus for the Macintosh. Because it sold so well, the Norton AntiVirus product for the PC was developed and became one of Symantec's best-sellers. Symantec was one of the first and most successful companies to use the Internet to fulfill customer needs, particularly with LiveUpdate, a Web-based service that enables customers to download updates for their security and utility products from Symantec's Website. In 1998 Symantec acquired enterprise antivirus technology from IBM and Intel, helping the company expand its reach to corporate customers.

In 1999 the board hired John W. Thompson, a senior IBM executive, as chairman and CEO. Thompson set a bold new direction for the company, stripping away some traditional product lines and focusing the company on the security business. Thompson also replaced much of the management team, centralized many decision-making processes, made employee reward structures more incentive based, and refocused Symantec as a business solutions–driven company. The strategy was a success. The company quickly became the leader in Internet security for both enterprises and consumers.

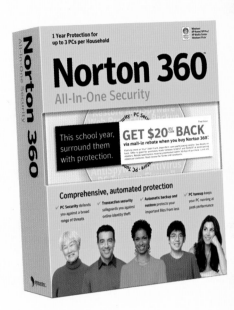

The company also grew tremendously by focusing on the opportunities of the Internet and anticipating the increased need for security for connected PCs. The company understood that corporate customers face increasingly sophisticated security attacks and wanted to provide a more proactive, comprehensive approach to security. This led to the acquisition of Axent Technologies in 2000 and later, as the security threat landscape shifted and Symantec redefined security to more broadly focus on protecting infrastructure, information, and interactions, to the acquisition of Veritas. Those two pivotal moves enabled Symantec to address additional timely enterprise concerns, including business continuity, regulatory compliance, IT risk management and data center management.

Symantec is now a global leader in infrastructure software, enabling businesses and consumers to have confidence in a connected world. Today Symantec helps enterprises and consumers protect their infrastructure, information, and interactions by delivering software and services that address risks to security, availability, compliance, and performance. Headquartered in Cupertino, Symantec has operations in 40 countries and is the fourth largest independent software company in the world.

John W. Thompson, President and CEO, 1999–Present

Komag Incorporated has a rich history as an independent supplier of thin-film disks, the disks in hard drives that store data in the magnetic layer on their surfaces. Founded in 1983, Komag has consistently been at the forefront of innovation, from pioneering recording technologies to manufacturing near the company's customers in Malaysia.

In true Silicon Valley style, Komag was established after several engineers at Xerox PARC learned their project to adapt thin-film technology to magnetic storage disks was cancelled. Their entrepreneurial endeavor was successful, and within a decade thin-film disks became the dominant data-storage technology.

Since its founding, Komag has continued to set records with the highest-performing thin-film disks on the market. Today, as the only public American magnetic media company, Komag continues to drive the evolution of magnetic recording as it works closely with its customers to consistently improve storage densities and recording performance. Given that Komag's customer base comprises 90% of the aluminum-based hard drives in the world, Komag has ample opportunity to advance innovation in all corners of the hard drive market.

With the proliferation of products that require high-capacity disk drives, Komag is positioned to capitalize on new opportunities worldwide. According to TrendFOCUS, conventional computer products will continue to grow and non-traditional storage applications such as DVRs and gaming consoles should contribute substantially to growth over the next five years. To power that growth, Komag will continue to provide extremely reliable, leading-edge technology that meets the needs of its customers.

Komag Incorporated was acquired by Western Digital Corporation in September 2007.

Komag retired CEO - TH Tan
(1999 to 2006)

Thin-film media for hard disk drives

Genentech's informal founding, over a couple of beers — cast in bronze.

enentech was founded in 1976, by Robert A. Swanson and the biochemist, Dr. Herbert W. Boyer. In the early 1970s, Stanley Cohen and Dr. Boyer had pioneered a new area of science called recombinant DNA technology.

Towards the end of 1975, Robert Swanson made a cold call to Dr. Herbert Boyer at his laboratory at the University of California – San Francisco.

> *"There was some discussion in a number of scientific journals on the potential of recombinant DNA technology to produce useful products. I started calling up scientists in different parts of the country at different universities because the science was all within the academic world at that point. He [Boyer] was the only one that I called who agreed with me at the time and thought that this science not only had potential, but something could be done immediately. I tried to convince him to see me, and he was very polite and nice, but he said that he was awfully busy. I said, 'No, you don't understand. You're the only one I've talked to that thinks something can be done now,' and finally he relented and said, 'Well, ten minutes on Friday afternoon.' I showed up at his lab at U.C. San Francisco in my suit, and everybody else was in jeans and, and T-shirts, and we hit it off. It turned into three or four hours and about that many beers. We found out that not only did we like each other, but we shared a common vision, and from that point, I went about putting together a business plan. We each put in our $500 and incorporated Genentech."*

> — *Robert Swanson, Founder, Genentech*

Genentech went on to develop a new generation of therapeutics developed from genetically engineered copies of naturally occurring molecules important in human health and disease. Genentech scientists have proved it is possible to make useful medicines by splicing genes into fast-growing bacteria that produce therapeutic proteins.

Today, Genentech is the leader in the field it created—its genetically engineered medicines are indispensable to modern health. In 2006, Genentech's revenues were $9.3 billion, a 40% increase from 2005.

The company slogan is: In business for life.

Members of the Maxim startup team in 1983 (back row (L-to-R): Dave Fullagar, Roger Fuller, Dave Bingham, Lee Evans, and Steve Combs; front row (L-to-R): Bev Fuller, Rich Hood, Fred Beck, Sam Ochi, and Jack Gifford)

hroughout its 25-year history, Maxim Integrated Products has prospered by maintaining an emphasis on proprietary, non-commodity products, end-market diversity, and tight control of the product development process. Even when the tech bubble burst, this world-wide leader in the design, development, and manufacture of analog, mixed-signal, high-frequency, and digital circuits continued to be very profitable and was able to maintain its innovative direction. Today the company has more than $2 billion in revenues, more than 50 offices worldwide, and over 35,000 satisfied customers.

For its first 24 years, Maxim was led by John (Jack) Gifford, a former UCLA baseball star and a pioneer in the analog semiconductor industry. Before founding Maxim, Gifford was the product manager for Fairchild's groundbreaking analog IC division, helped Intersil get into the analog data-acquisition business, and, after General Electric purchased Intersil, was president of GE-Intersil. Gifford also cofounded AMD.

In 1983, Gifford started Maxim with pioneering colleagues, including Fred Beck, Dave Fullagar, Dave Bingham, Steve Combs, Lee Evans, Roger Fuller, Rich Hood, and Dick Wilenken. Beck, an IC sales and distribution pioneer, had been the co-founder of distribution company Hamilton-Avnet. Fullagar had invented the first compensated op amp IC at Fairchild Semiconductor in 1968. Bingham introduced the first CMOS power-supply circuits and the first counter and timer products and co-developed the first single-chip digital voltmeter IC with Maxim co-founder Lee Evans. Bingham was General Electric's "Scientist of the Year" in 1982 and was also named "Designer of the Year" by *Electronics Magazine*. Combs, who designed and built major wafer manufacturing facilities, had developed innovative CMOS IC technologies for HP.

Evans, who also co-founded Siliconix and Intech, was a pioneer in CMOS products and developed the first monolithic CMOS chopper-stabilized amplifier and the first monolithic 16-bit ADC. Along with Dave Bingham, Evans was General Electric's "Scientist of the Year" in 1982. Roger Fuller was a pioneer CMOS designer at Intersil, where he developed the first monolithic display drivers and some of the earliest timer and counter products. He subsequently worked at AMCC and as an independent consultant. As Intersil's director of Product and Test Engineering, Hood directed the development of one of the first microprocessor-controlled automatic test systems in existence, as well as proprietary laser-trim systems and methods for enhanced product precision and accuracy. These innovations enabled substantially improved product performance and world-class manufacturing costs. Wilenken, acknowledged as the father of CMOS analog switches and multiplexers, designed the first monolithic CMOS switch to replace hybrids and also invented the virtual ground switch concept.

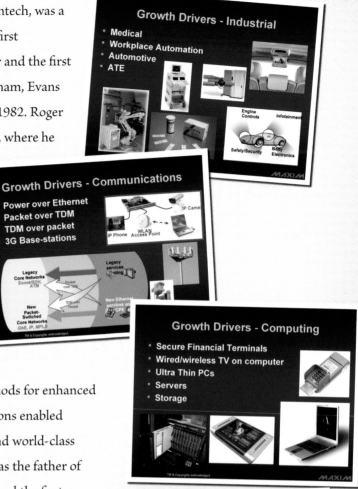

Gifford and his co-founders' vision for Maxim was to provide high-quality analog and mixed-signal engineering solutions to the technology industry. Though the market was already crowded with several major players, including Texas Instruments, National Semiconductor, Fairchild, and Analog Devices, the Maxim team prevailed: On the strength of a two-page, hand-written business plan—and the strong industry reputations of the founders—$9 million in venture capital was raised and the fledgling company got right to work.

Gifford began by challenging his small team to produce at least 15 new products each quarter. An aggressive product proliferation policy has been in place ever since, resulting in over 5,400 products across more than 70 product lines. Through its many innovations, Maxim now serves over 20 end markets, including automatic test equipment, automotive, cellular base stations, digital cameras, cell phones,

A Maxim EOL facility in the Philippines

smartphones, computing and peripherals, financial terminals, home entertainment and appliances, industrial, instrumentation and measurement, medical, military, networking and data communications, notebook computers, set-top boxes, storage, telecommunications, and many more.

Maxim became successful right at the start, and grew quickly through the 1980s. That decade saw Maxim not only going public—it was among the first companies to do so after the "Black Monday" crash of 1987, reflecting Maxim's strength and confidence—but also establishing offices in the U.K., Japan, France, and Germany, and purchasing its first wafer fab. Maxim launched its first proprietary product in 1985, winning *EDN Magazine's* "Innovation of the Year." Maxim's introduction of the MAX232 serial interface IC in 1986 established the single-chip, single supply-voltage RS-232 serial interface market. This product was designed by Dave Bingham, based on a market opportunity identified by Charlie Allen. It's overwhelming commercial success put Maxim on the map.

During the following decade, which would include the dot-com boom, Maxim saw another period of outstanding growth. The company opened several more sales and development offices in Europe and Asia, established manufacturing test operations in the Philippines, and introduced its first high-integration notebook power-supply IC (MAX782). That

A manufacturing test floor at Maxim

groundbreaking product, designed by Tunç Doluca, who would later succeed Jack Gifford as CEO, earned Maxim access into the notebook electronics market. Many follow-on, high-performance products resulted in Maxim's dominance in the notebook power management market for over a decade.

Though in earlier years Maxim had been associated with only a few key products, the company's reputation significantly expanded by the mid-90s, and orders began to flow in for a wide variety of products. Maxim's growth drivers in this period were state-of-the-art products for computing applications and, in the late 1990s, communications infrastructure. Just after the turn of the millennium, the company acquired Dallas Semiconductor, expanding its engineering base and its product lines even further. In particular, Maxim gained a new core of expertise in digital circuits, which enabled an expansion into higher-integration, mixed-signal products.

Since that time, Maxim has continued to grow, expanding its product offering to include high-volume, high-end consumer applications, establishing many more domestic and international design centers, and expanding its manufacturing capacity to six wafer fabs and three offshore EOL facilities. Its large stable of proprietary technologies now gives the company a great advantage in the marketplace. Although founded last among its peer group, Maxim's superior growth has enabled it to vie for the position of second-largest supplier of analog/mixed-signal products in the world today. Maxim's current growth drivers are improved replacement products for formerly mechanical applications, industrial products, communications products, computing products, and high-end consumer products.

The year 2007 saw the first leadership change at Maxim: Jack Gifford retired and Tunç Doluca became president and CEO. Doluca joined Maxim in 1983 as a design engineer and personally designed several key products. Now, as president and CEO, Doluca remains committed to ensuring Maxim's continued growth and industry leadership and to pursuing the company's original mission: to continuously invent the best possible analog and mixed-signal engineering solutions, to add value to its customers' microprocessor-based electronics, and to enable their customers' next generation of innovative, high-performance end-equipment.

Jack Gifford (left) and
Tunç Doluca (right)

A s a leading global provider of digital solutions for the growing digital entertainment and digital imaging markets, Zoran Corporation has operations in Canada, China, England, Germany, India, Israel, Japan, Korea and the U.S. It is appropriate that this cutting-edge company has its headquarters in Sunnyvale, the center of Silicon Valley—the word "Zoran" is derived from the Hebrew, the oldest word for "silicon."

Led by co-founder, president, and CEO Dr. Levy Gerzberg, Zoran has been developing and delivering digital signal processing (DSP) technologies and solutions for the home, office, and mobile consumer since 1983. From its start, the company has pioneered high-performance digital applications that enable original equipment manufacturers (OEMs) to bring innovative electronic products to consumers around the world. Zoran delivers high quality system-on-a-chip solutions incorporating unique algorithms and software that enable OEMs to bring to market high quality DVD players and recorders, digital cameras, multimedia mobile phones, digital televisions and set top boxes, digital printers and other emerging categories of consumer devices. In addition, Zoran is focused on delivering technologies that allow consumers to connect and share their video and audio files with their families and friends while improving their digital entertainment experiences in their homes, offices or while traveling.

Dr. Levy Gerzberg surrounded by consumer products powered by Zoran.

Many of Zoran's products and technologies were the first to market. In 1985, Zoran introduced the first Vector Signal Processors and high performance Digital Filters which broke new performance records for high-speed applications in military, medical and industrial imaging. In 1989, the company developed the first digital camera chip-set. In 1992, Zoran delivered the first JPEG image and video compression technology for desk-top video editing. In 1994, it was the first to market a single-chip IC that implemented six-channel Dolby Digital surround-sound audio for home and movie theater applications, and in 1997, it introduced the first DVD chip with integrated Dolby Digital audio. Since the year 2000, Zoran has increased its pace of firsts: it developed the first networked DVD player, the first HDTV processor for high-definition TVs and set-top boxes; enabled the first recyclable digital video camera for under $30 and the first multimedia co-processor with 5 megapixel image capture in mobile phones.

Zoran's state-of-the-art technology has received high marks and powered many award-winning products. Its COACH digital camera processor, incorporating image-stabilization and anti-blur technology, enables Samsung's Digimax i6 PMP digital camera, the first digital still camera that also functions as a video camera, video player, or music player. Its Zmedia-based technology powers the portable video recorder that was named Best of Show at Macworld 2006.

Zoran-based products, including those with the company's Connect Share Entertain™ technologies, can now be found in hundreds of millions of homes and offices worldwide. To continue its record growth and success, this Deloitte Fast 50 Silicon Valley growth company plans to continue focusing on delivering major benefits to its OEM customers, including greater product capabilities, reduced system costs, and shorter time to market, and to delivering technologies that enable consumers to have the best possible digital entertainment experiences.

Zoran delivers the first single-chip IC implementing six-channel Dolby Digital surround-sound audio for home and movie theater applications.

F or nearly 25 years, IXYS Corporation has been a stalwart of Silicon Valley. The innovation and technological expertise that define the area have been intrinsic to the success of IXYS, a recognized leader in the power semiconductor industry.

Diminishing natural resources, demand for cheap electricity and environmental directives for energy efficiency represent a significant challenge. IXYS addresses those demands, developing technology-driven products to improve power conversion efficiency. IXYS is a U.S. pioneer in the development of power semiconductors, mixed-signal integrated circuits and RF power systems that effectively manage electrical voltage to produce maximum effect with the least expenditure of energy.

IXYS is a key provider of solutions for alternative and renewable energy sources.

Today, IXYS' products are embedded in everyday applications, ranging from telecommunications, transportation, industrial, medical, consumer/white goods to renewable energy industries. IXYS' products are essential to VoIP equipment, wind energy conversion systems, medical imaging machines, defibrillators, high-speed transit and much more.

Process controls help IXYS achieve the highest quality.

With a singular focus on power conversion efficiency, IXYS explored other sources of electrical power including solar and wind energy. For nearly 15 years, IXYS has been introducing products to harness wind and solar power for conversion to the U.S. electrical power grid. Recently, the company developed solar cell arrays and cards for charging portable batteries – with applications for traditional alkaline batteries, laptops, cell phones, RFID tags and sensors, to name a few.

In recognition of these efforts, IXYS ranked among *Business 2.0 Magazine's* "100 Fastest-Growing Technology Companies" in its June 2007 issue. In April of this year, IXYS Corporation was selected as one of 15 California Innovation Award recipients, recognized by California Tech 100 partners and the California Commission on Jobs and Economic Growth. In 2006, IXYS was named as one of "Silicon Valley Deloitte Technology Fast 50", whereby Deloitte & Touche recognized the fastest growing technology companies in Silicon Valley.

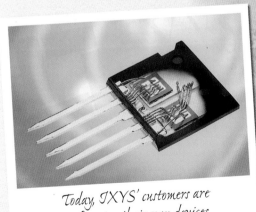

Today, IXYS' customers are configuring their own devices.

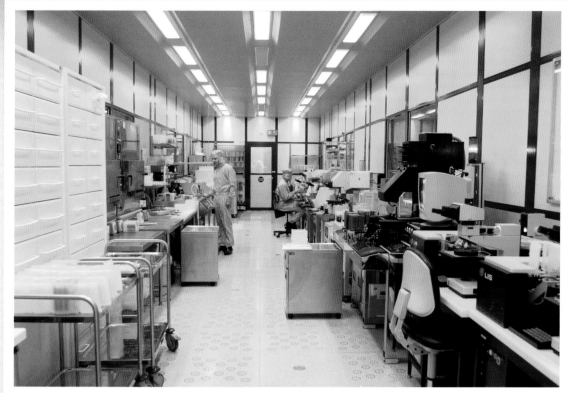

IXYS utilizes precision to speed the pace of innovation.

Behind these accolades is IXYS' Founder, Chairman and CEO Dr. Nathan Zommer. Since IXYS' inception in 1983, Dr. Zommer has been an advocate of energy-efficient technologies as strategic investment opportunities. After receiving his PhD in electrical engineering from Carnegie Mellon University, with a research emphasis on power transistors, Dr. Zommer started his career working with HP Labs in Palo Alto, CA. Dr. Zommer went on to join Intersil to develop the Power MOS division. When Intersil was acquired by General Electric in 1981, Dr. Zommer teamed with Dr. Jayant B. Baliga as part of the GE CRD team to pursue the practical realization of IGBTs. Dr. Zommer and Dr. Baliga designed and fabricated the first IGBT. In 1983, Dr. Zommer branched out to form IXYS Corporation.

Today, IXYS is a $286 million annual revenue business, with multi-disciplined technology spanning the entire power spectrum from MOS, Bipolar, SOI, DCB, IGBTs, ICs to RF systems and beyond. IXYS, and its subsidiary companies, employ more than 1000 people in eight divisions across the globe, and offer a diversified product base that addresses worldwide needs for power conversion, electrical efficiency and renewable energy.

"Over the next 10 years, demand for electricity is expected to grow 3x as fast as supply; a power gap will persist. In that spirit, IXYS will continue to deploy new products to solve global energy needs, introducing new technologies in the heart of Silicon Valley," commented Dr. Zommer.

IXYS products play a vital role in reducing energy consumption.

tmel® is a worldwide leader in the design and manufacture of microcontrollers, mixed-signal, ASICs, nonvolatile memory and radio frequency (RF) silicon chips. Leveraging one of the industry's broadest intellectual property (IP) portfolios, Atmel provides electronics systems and device manufacturers with complete system solutions. This level of service to the industry enables Atmel's customers to lead the markets they serve with electronic products that are smaller, smarter, more cost-effective and versatile than ever before. The company's success over the last 27 years is a result of its focus on high-growth electronic-equipment markets across the spectrum of applications: consumer, communications, computer/network, security, industrial, automotive, as its slogan states, the company is "Everywhere You Are.®" Its extensive network of R&D, design, manufacturing, engineering, sales, and distribution facilities enables it to reach customers in over 60 countries.

Originally founded in 1984, Atmel was an early pioneer of NVM (nonvolatile memory) chips that retain their content in the absence of power. Atmel, with its broad NVM family offering, is the industry's leading supplier of serial interface memories (i.e. SEE and DataFlash®). The family range in memory size from 1k-bits to mega-bits and is offered in leading edge packages for applications where board space and height is important.

Atmel has developed a broad portfolio of products to meet the system solution requirements of its customers. These products range from custom to standard products and are available in industrial or automotive grade. The solutions include microcontrollers, RF, automotive products, ASICs, products with security (i.e. encryption), and non-volatile memories.

As the first company to successfully embed its EEPROM non-volatile memory technology (#1 in market share) into the world's first Flash-based microcontroller, Atmel has continued to lead the way in microcontroller technology. As we look to the future, Atmel's microcontroller product lines feature the industry-leading AVR® advanced 8-bit RISC microcontroller family providing instruction and data throughputs many times those of traditional CISC architectures. AVR features extensive on-chip analog and digital peripherals together with in-system programmable EE-

Atmel Headquarters

PROM and Flash memories, greatly increasing flexibility, eliminating the bottleneck of external memory accesses, and providing increased program and data security. The series ranges from the tinyAVR™ (1K bytes of on-chip Flash) to the megaAVR™ (128K bytes of on-chip Flash), and it's ultra low power AVR family.

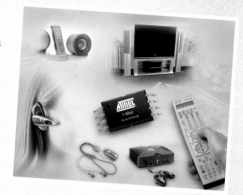

For applications requiring superior processing capability while keeping power consumption to a minimum, Atmel offers a wide range of 32-bit microcontrollers based on the ARM® advanced RISC core and it's AVR32 core. This series offers a variety of memory sizes and on-chip functionality in order to meet the precise requirements of many high-performance applications.

Atmel also has developed a family of secure products that addresses different levels of security and applications. Such products are its Crypto family, biometrics, TPM (Trusted Platform Module) and secure smart card chips using its AVR® 8-bit RISC and ARM processors.

Atmel's automotive products support an application portfolio that includes body electronics (e.g., bus systems such as LIN/CAN, and driver ICs), car access, theft protection (remote keyless entry/immobilizer), airbag and tire-pressure monitoring systems, and infotainment.

Atmel's radio frequency (RF) products comprise front-end devices (transmitters, receivers, and transceivers), as well as single-chip RF ICs with integrated ARM or AVR microcontrollers. Applications include car access, industrial ISM, ZigBee™ and other wireless data connectivity systems.

Atmel is a world leader in microcontrollers, offering both stand-alone or embedded solutions. These solutions address both the commercial, industrial, and automotive markets. Atmel also offers products for those applications which require security or RF technology. The company provides complete system solutions, such as a system-in-a package (SiP) and a system-on-a-chip (SoC), by capitalizing on its core strengths. The company has maintained its competitive edge in process technology by focusing strongly on research and development and collaborating with top universities and key clients. Through its commitment to its customers and its support of their products, Atmel will continue to lead the way in global innovation, producing ICs that enable customers to rapidly introduce leading edge electronic products.

Atmel® ATmega48, ATmega88, ATmega168 and AT90CAN128
First Automotive Qualified Flash AVR® Microcontrollers

that enable the networking of health information and the creation of regional and national health care networks.

Through its culture of innovation, Cisco also enables students in more than 160 countries to follow their own educational and professional dreams. The Cisco Networking Academy Program trains students to design, build, and maintain networks, helping them to gain the skills they need for higher education and to land

Fast growing Cisco Systems moved in 1994 to this San Jose headquarters.

IT-related jobs. The company also participates in the Jordan Education Initiative, an e-learning project in cooperation with the World Economic Forum and the Kingdom of Jordan that promises to be a model to improve education in many countries. Through these and many other projects, and through extensive R&D, Cisco is continuing to fulfill its promise to transform the way people connect, communicate, collaborate, and grow.

anta Clara-based PMC-Sierra, Inc. is a leading semiconductor company that enables the world's next-generation communications infrastructure. PMC-Sierra is a leader in Fiber to the Home semiconductors and enterprise storage system solutions for networked and server storage applications.

The company was originally founded as Sierra Semiconductor in 1984 and was focused on semiconductor solutions for the personal computer market. In 1994, Sierra Semiconductor acquired a Canadian start-up called PMC-Sierra, which was developing an innovative line of broadband communications semiconductors. A few years later, Sierra Semiconductor made the strategic decision to exit the PC-oriented business and focus on the broadband communications opportunity. As a result, the company changed its name to PMC-Sierra (NASDAQ: PMCS) to reflect this new direction. PMC-Sierra is registered in the State of Delaware and its headquarters are located in Santa Clara, California.

After experiencing the telecommunications industry downturn that began around 2001, PMC-Sierra concentrated

PMC-Sierra's technology platforms are enabling connectivity worldwide.

on maximizing operating efficiencies to return to profitability while positioning the company for future growth. The company continued to diversify by expanding its customer base in Asia and growing its enterprise storage business. In 2006, the company acquired the storage semiconductor business from Avago Technologies (formerly the semiconductor business of Agilent Technologies), which brought a leadership position in Fibre Channel controllers to complement PMC-Sierra's existing Fibre Channel disk interconnect products for the enterprise storage market. Today, PMC-Sierra offers the industry's highest performance end-to-end Fibre Channel solutions as well as industry-leading serial-attached SCSI (SAS) and serial ATA (SATA) products.

In 2006, the company also acquired Passave Inc., the leading system-on-chip (SoC) semiconductor supplier to the Fiber to the Home access market. As the only supplier with millions of gigabit PON devices in field deployment and a portfolio that supports all major high-speed FTTx technologies, including EPON (IEEE802.3ah Ethernet in the First Mile), GPON (ITU-T G.984), Gigabit Ethernet, VDSL2, and ADSL2+, PMC-Sierra supports fiber access deployments in all geographic markets using any network topology.

PMC-Sierra has the architectural experience to provide a wide range of cutting-edge solutions by leveraging its extensive intellectual property and using innovative cross-platform design teams that

Recognized as an industry leader, PMC-Sierra attracts talented and motivated individuals.

work collaboratively around the world. The company maintains its growing customer base by providing top-level technical and sales support through its offices in North America, Europe, Israel, and Asia.

Over the years, PMC-Sierra has evolved from a PC-focused business to a widely diversified international organization with leadership in next-generation infrastructure, enterprise storage, and Fiber to the Home solutions. The company has enhanced its technology platforms and growth prospects through strategic investments in research and development as well as key acquisitions. With a strong management team, PMC-Sierra is leading the communications semiconductor industry by providing the enabling technologies that capture, process, store, and transmit information that will drive the next wave of the Digital Age.

Company headquarters are located in Santa Clara, California.

In 1984, Xilinx founders set forth a lofty goal: "To be the leading company designing, manufacturing, marketing, and supporting user-configurable logic arrays for the application-specific market." Back then, configurable logic arrays were exotic curiosities, the industry was in a slump, and the PC (destined to become the driving force in silicon consumption) was being introduced to skeptical reviews.

Without a doubt, Xilinx founders Ross Freeman, Bernie Vonderschmitt, and Jim Barnett made good on their promise. Today, the company that virtually invented the FPGA (field programmable gate array) is the preeminent supplier of programmable chips, with more than 50% market share. Now, the mantra driving its 3,500+ employees is: *"To put a programmable solution into every electronic system."*

Talk to Chairman, CEO, and President Wim Roelandts about leadership and you won't hear chest-thumping or a litany of firsts and bests. In keeping with the legacy of Bernie Vonderschmitt, who served as CEO for a dozen years before becoming chairman in 1996 and retiring in 2003, Roelandts speaks passionately about core values, humility, walking the walk. Little wonder that an equally important goal today is: *"To build a company that sets a standard for managing high-tech companies."*

Xilinx founder Bernie Vonderschmitt

Roelandts' style draws upon years of experience at Hewlett-Packard, renowned for its "HP Way" culture. At the helm of Xilinx since 1996, Roelandts worked hand-in-hand with Vonderschmitt to combine the best of traditional hard-driving management approaches with a softer, people-centric management philosophy: people want to do a good job and do their best work; work must have meaning and value; a company must provide a sense of community; there must be an opportunity for personal growth; and everyone should be an owner.

The commitment of Xilinx to its employees has become the stuff of legend in Silicon Valley, most notably its no-layoff policy after the Internet "bubble" burst in 2001. Such courage earned the company a spot near the top of *FORTUNE* magazine's "Top 100 Best Places to Work" list for five straight years.

But all the talk of values would mean nothing if Xilinx wasn't producing results. "We can have a culture where people are treated with respect and still be a leader," says Roelandts. "How do you do it? Through innovation! With innovation comes leadership."

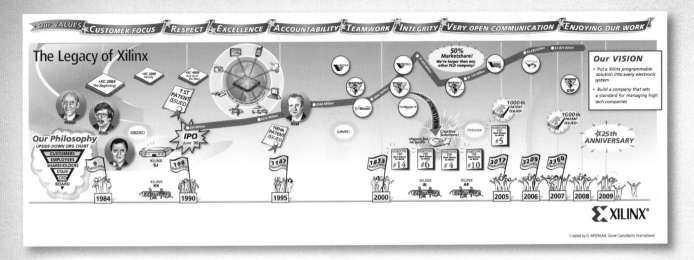

For nearly 25 years, the company has set new standards for semiconductor design. More than 1,600 patents grace the company's San Jose headquarters on its legendary "patent wall." Such achievements began with a focus on doing a few things—and doing them well.

From the beginning, the company's strategy relied on a partnership model. Vonderschmitt essentially invented the fabless semiconductor model on a handshake agreement with Seiko in 1985, with the first-ever Xilinx-designed chips rolling off the manufacturing lines at the Japanese electronics giant's plants. Since then, Xilinx has developed an extensive ecosystem of partnerships in manufacturing, sales, design tools, intellectual property (IP) cores, and chip design services.

Roelandts likes to call Xilinx a reconfigurable company. Of the challenge of keeping Xilinx nimble and responsive, he says, "Every day we change. Whether it's the technology, a business process, or geographical focus…you have to be comfortable with change and re-innovate from within."

What else would you expect from the company that invented programmable chips?

Wim Roelandts, Chairman, CEO and President

Chapter 14 (1985 to 1987): Clouds Over Silicon Valley

Clouds cast dark shadows over Silicon Valley in the mid-'80s, prompting fear its heyday had passed. But beneath the surface gloom, seeds of regenerative growth sprouted.

A slump struck the U.S. semiconductor industry in 1985, and in 1986 it worsened. In the same era, U.S. minicomputer makers, largely based in Massachusetts, began to reel under the impact of workstations and powerful personal computers.

Such U.S. semiconductor leaders as Intel, AMD, and National Semiconductor withdrew from memory chip production in 1985. Beset by a glutted market, signs of formidable Japanese manufacturing prowess, and alleged Japanese dumping of standard chips, they conceded defeat in commodity manufacturing. They lost heavily, but not so heavily as Japanese firms remaining in the field.

U.S. executives' pleas for government protection against dumping culminated in the U.S.-Japan Semiconductor Trade Agreement of 1986, which set floor prices on memory devices and encouraged opening of Japanese markets to U.S. products. In hindsight, this pact has been widely regarded as too little, too late—or entirely ill-founded. It caused a DRAM shortage that hurt U.S. computer firms. Some observers saw the U.S. semiconductor industry as facing extinction by the Japanese, much as the U.S. automobile, steel, and consumer electronics industries had been eclipsed.

Space Shuttle Challenger

Another cloud dimmed the space frontier. By the end of 1985, the U.S. space shuttle fleet — boasting four orbiters after Atlantis made its 1985 maiden flight — had logged 21 missions. Then on January 28, 1986, disaster befell the program when Challenger exploded shortly after launch, killing six astronauts and teacher Christa McAuliffe. The tragedy rocked public confidence in NASA and caused a two-year hold while the manned flight program was overhauled.

IBM was nibbled by swarms of clone PC manufacturers, but Big Blue and other U.S. systems firms brought lustrous new entries of their own to the marketplace. In 1985, Hewlett-Packard introduced what was destined to become its most successful single product: the HP LaserJet printer.

In 1986, IBM announced the first commercial RISC (reduced instruction set computer), the RT/PC workstation. A year later, IBM introduced its PS/2 personal computer with 3.5-inch disk drives, which would soon supplant 5.25-inch floppy disks as the industry standard.

Intel's 80386 microprocessor, a high-speed 32-bit chip announced in 1985, was brought to market first in 1986 by Compaq Computer, which beat IBM to the punch. Earlier, Intel had licensed AMD as a second source for its microprocessors, but in the case of the 80386, Intel sought to remain the sole supplier — a stand that resulted in protracted litigation.

Apple Computer continued to ride high with the popular Macintosh. In software, desktop publishing came to the

1985
Mikhail Gorbachev elected Soviet Communist party leader; introduces reforms.

Earthquake in Mexico City kills 10,000.

1986
Chernobyl nuclear power disaster in the U.S.S.R.

Disaster of U.S. space shuttle Challenger.

U.S bombs Libya in retaliation of terrorist acts.

Glasnost and Perestroika initiated in U.S.S.R.

- 120 -

fore. Aldus Corp's PageMaker for the Mac became a top seller.

Meanwhile, Silicon Valley start-ups grew in mass. SynOptics Communications, a company commercializing Xerox PARC technology, was founded in 1985 by Andrew Ludwick, Ronald Schmidt and Shelby Carter. Its fiber-optics local area networks enabled computers to talk on the telephone.

Xerox PARC

Early '80s start-ups were making their competitive impact felt. Within five years, the collective revenues of the new CMOS firms exceeded Intel and AMD CMOS revenues put together and afforded the United States a large base of advanced CMOS production skills. Such innovations prompted William J. Perry — engineer, venture capitalist and future Secretary of Defense — to predict a hundredfold drop in the cost of computing over the next decade.

Along with new products and technology, changes were afoot in the way Silicon Valley worked. Drawing lessons from the giant semiconductor firms era of sterile isolation, companies began to return to the close collaboration that marked the Valley in the 1960s and '70s. For example, in 1987, Hewlett-Packard opened its foundry for the first time to an outside firm, Weitek, a design specialist supplier.

Warhead disassembly

At about the same time, some recent start-ups were building minifabs designed for short runs at modest cost. Contract manufacturer Flextronics completed its evolution from consignment to turnkey operations. Solectron developed surface-mount technology, enabling the use of smaller, two-sided circuit boards. Apple advanced desktop technology.

Sematech formed in 1987 as an industry-government partnership to share the cost of developing new micro-electronic devices such as ASIC and RISC chips. A decision to locate this semiconductor manufacturing institute in Austin, Texas, disappointed Silicon Valley. Foes of a U.S. industrial policy decried big federal investments in it.

Globally, change was also evident. In a breakthrough stemming partly from Mikhail Gorbachev's rise to power, the Soviet Union and the United States agreed in 1987 to dismantle ballistic missiles with ranges of 300 to 4,000 miles. The long Cold War showed promise of winding down.

1987

Haleys comet passed by the Sun for the first time in 76 years.

World stock markets crash.

Berlin Wall is torn down.

U.S. troops invade Panama.

Gorbachev and Reagan summit resulting in the elimination of

intermediate range nuclear missiles.

Home users, businesses, Internet service providers, and government agencies all rely on McAfee's unmatched computer security expertise and proven security solutions. This leading dedicated security company, headquartered in Santa Clara, California, proactively secures systems and networks from known and unknown threats, empowering customers to block attacks, prevent disruptions, and continuously track and improve their security.

Named for its founder, John McAfee, the company was formed in 1987 as McAfee Associates. British-born McAfee, while working at Lockheed in the 1980s, had received a copy of a computer virus and had soon begun developing software to combat such scourges. First working from his home, he established McAfee Associates as an anti-virus company. Today, McAfee is the largest dedicated security company in the world.

McAfee provides an arsenal of superior security products, including anti-virus, anti-spam, anti-spyware, data-loss prevention, encryption, host-intrusion prevention, mobile security, and messaging and e-mail security. Together these products provide a comprehensive security risk-management solution that is integrated, automated, reliable, and actionable. While security threats keep changing, McAfee's experience, expertise, and innovation help its customers stay one step ahead.

McAfee's suite of threat-prevention products includes the ePolicy Orchestrator®, a one-of-a-kind centralized management console that provides a single view of multiple security products. Its Total Protection product, for home and business use, provides complete online and PC security, stopping wireless intruders, identity theft, spammers, and hackers as well as intercepting prohibited Websites and automating print and file sharing among trusted users. The company's SiteAdvisor Plus advises users about the safety of Websites and their downloads, disables all interaction with dangerous sites, and updates automatically to protect against new threats.

Since its founding, McAfee has changed its name and bought and sold companies several times. Ten years after its founding, the company became Network Associates when it merged with Network General. In 2004 the company sold its Magic Solutions business to Remedy, a subsidiary of BMC Software, and also sold its Sniffer Technologies business to a venture-capital-backed firm with a familiar name—Network General. In 2005 the company was renamed McAfee, Inc., to reflect its intensified focus on security-related technologies.

Through all the changes, McAfee has remained committed to creating best in class computer security solutions that prevent intrusions on networks and protect computer systems from the next generation of attacks and threats. With president and CEO David DeWalt leading the way, the company also remains committed to being a good corporate citizen and giving back to the communities in which its employees live and work. McAfee provides financial grants as well as donations of employee time, products, and expertise. And by doing business at the highest level of integrity and ethics, McAfee has not only had numerous products chosen as finalists in SC Magazine's "Best Intrusion Solution" and "Best Anti-Virus Solution" categories but been named "Technology Gazelle of the Year" for its more than 250 patents as well as "Best Employer" in CMP Media's third-annual Software Development Reader's Choice Awards.

McAfee headquarters in Santa Clara, California.

I n true Silicon Valley style, SanDisk Corporation was founded by a man with a passion for technology in modest surroundings and on a very short shoestring. Dr. Eli Harari, an Israel-born physicist and internationally recognized authority on non-volatile flash memory technology, created SanDisk, first known as SunDisk, in 1988, with partners Sanjay Mehrotra and Jack Yuan. Along with 10 employees, the trio worked from a converted stock brokerage office in Sunnyvale, Calif., and the company became profitable only after four years of struggle. Since those early days SanDisk has come a long way—it's now among the world's largest producers of flash memory data storage products, with more than 2,500 employees and $3 billion in sales as of 2007.

The first product the fledging company offered was a PC card that looked like a circuit board and was as large as a person's hand. The card contained all of 10 megabytes of memory, the equivalent capacity of seven floppy disks. Just six years after its founding, however, SanDisk brought to market the first flash memory card, the CompactFlash®, which was much smaller and much more powerful.

Another technology breakthrough came in 1998, when Dr. Harari and his team used a multi-level cell, or double density, process they developed that enabled two bits of data to be recorded on each of the card's transistors. The process made it possible to store twice the amount of data in each cell.

SanDisk went public in 1995 and began to grow rapidly. By the late 1990s, it had opened offices in Israel, Hong Kong, Japan and Germany. In 2005 it opened a design center in India and in 2006 the company moved its Europe/Middle East/Africa offices to Dublin, Ireland. New, larger company headquarters were also established in Milpitas in 2006.

Since the mid-'90s, SanDisk's line of flash memory products has also grown rapidly—it now has the largest and most diverse line in the industry. The company designs, develops, manufactures, and markets flash memory cards in every major format for a wide variety of digital devices, including digital cameras; mobile phones; PDAs and handheld computers; portable game, video, and music players; GPS navigation devices; and USB flash

SanDisk SSD (solid state drive) with a Dell laptop computer. Dell was the first company to announce a SanDisk SSD option as a replacement for a hard drive on its ultralight computers.

SanDisk CEO Eli Harari tries out a Ducati motorcycle during a press conference at the SanDisk Milpitas headquarters on July 18, 2007, announcing the launch of the new SanDisk branded line of Extreme Ducati Edition flash memory cards and USB drive.

drives. Its flash devices are indispensable because they have no moving parts, store data in microscopic cells of razor-thin chips, require no power to retain information, and can be quickly erased.

The CompactFlash remains one of the most sought-after cards SanDisk produces, along with the SD™ and Memory Stick PRO™. To meet the memory storage needs of full-featured mobile phones, the company also offers even smaller but immensely powerful cards: the miniSD™, the Memory Stick PRO Duo™, and the even tinier microSD™, a fingernail-sized module that is now the world's smallest memory card and is available in capacities up to 8 gigabytes. In 2005, neon-colored Memory Stick PRO Duo gaming cards were added to SanDisk's line to use with the new Sony PlayStation Portable® (PSP™). The company expects increasing sales of these cards to power the Sony PlayStation 3 and the new Nintendo Wii game consoles.

SanDisk also develops and markets a line of USB flash drives, which includes the Cruzer® Contour, Cruzer Micro; Cruzer Titanium; and Cruzer Crossfire for gaming. In addition, the company has developed several card readers, including the 12-in-1 Multi-card Reader, the MobileMate™, the SD/MultiMediaCard™, and Memory Stick™ readers.

Another growing SanDisk line is its Sansa™ MP3 players, including the Sansa Clip, Sansa Shaker and Sansa View. These flash-based players let users play music, and – in some models – watch video clips and digital still photos on a sharp color screen. Available in capacities as high as 16 GB, the players can hold as many as 4,000 songs in their internal memory, and many Sansa models have a microSD card slot for extra capacity.

Early 2005 saw several exciting firsts at SanDisk. The company introduced the SanDisk Ultra® SD Plus, a dual-purpose SD memory card that has built-in USB connectivity. The company also dedicated Fab 3, a large manufacturing facility constructed in Yokkaichi, Japan, with Toshiba Corporation, to produce NAND flash memory on 300mm wafers, supporting the growing need for devices with higher memory capacities. SanDisk also launched, with M-Systems, the U3™ platform. U3 enables a number of software applications to run from a USB drive inserted in a personal computer, without leaving behind any personal information. SanDisk made available Cruzer Micro and Cruzer Titanium drives with U3 technology.

SanDisk headquarters in Milpitas, California.

Sansa e200 portable media player was SanDisk's first MP3 player that also played videos and still images on a bright, full-color screen. Equipped with an FM radio and voice recorder, this device is offered in several capacities, with the highest at 8 gigabytes. The Sansa e200 also has a slot for SanDisk's smallest flash card - the micro SD card - so that on-board memory can be supplemented.

In 2006, SanDisk introduced the SanDisk Extreme® IV, the world's fastest, highest-performing flash memory card. This came a year after SanDisk unveiled a 4GB monolithic NAND flash memory chip, based on breakthrough 90-nanometer technology.

In September 2007, SanDisk and Toshiba dedicated Fab 4 in Yokkaichi, which is expected to be the world's largest NAND fab.

SanDisk today is the world's number one producer of flash memory cards. Though the majority of sales come from the digital photography arena, the company is number one in sales of USB flash drives in the U.S. It is also the second largest manufacturer of MP3 players in the U.S.

With so much growth, it's no wonder that the *San Francisco Chronicle* ranked SanDisk number one in its 2004 rating of the top 200 companies in northern California. With the company's continuing focus on innovation and performance, it's also no wonder that consumers across the globe choose digital devices that house SanDisk memory products to reliably store their important information. As they say "Yes" to SanDisk's new slogan, "Store Your World in Ours™," they're meeting their own memory needs as well as enabling SanDisk to meet its goals.

Chapter 15: Networking Emerges; Cold War Ends

Perestroika (restructuring) and gladnost (openness) drastically reshaped the Soviet Union's government in 1988, lifting Mikhail Gorbachev to the presidency. In 1989, the winds of change became tornadoes, toppling the Berlin Wall and blowing away Communist regimes in East Germany, Hungary, Poland, Czechoslovakia, Bulgaria, and Romania.

The 40-year Cold War was over, in effect, although the Soviet Union itself did not finally collapse until 1991. The military stand-down shrank Silicon Valley defense contracts—a painful but not paralyzing blow to the regional economy.

During the late '80s, development of increasingly powerful desktop workstations lifted Silicon Valley to the leadership of the U.S. computer industry, surpassing the microcomputer manufacturers based near Boston. Sophisticated data management programs such as those of Oracle Systems enabled office workers to use high-performance desktop computers linked in networks, rather than the costly minicomputers of yore. A group's most powerful PC acted as a "server," or shared filing cabinet, for the network's data.

Optical fiber, the same material AT&T installed in an undersea cable linking the U.S. and Europe, helped improve local area networks (LANs).

Progress of microchip technology advanced development of the Integrated Services Digital Network (ISDN), which promised to integrate voice, data, text, and video communications in a single worldwide network employing digital rather than analog technology.

Parallel processing with multiple microprocessors also came to the fore. At NASA Ames in 1989, parallel processing nearly matched the performance of advanced supercomputers.

By the end of 1989, Sun Microsystems claimed to be the world's largest supplier of RISC (reduced instruction set chip) computers; MIPS Computers was close behind. A year before, the two companies had opened their respective RISC architectures for license to other computer makers. Meanwhile, Hewlett-Packard claimed the highest revenues

MIPS RISC-based processors

from the sale of RISC-based computers, and became the No. 1 work station vendor after buying out Apollo Computers of Chelmsford, Massachusetts, the original work station maker.

Intel Corporation unveiled its i486 microprocessor in 1989, and IBM and Compaq raced to market 486 PCs. Intel also introduced a new microprocessor for RISC architecture, the i860, containing more than 1 million transistors.

Despite the RISC and work station wars, 1989 ended with the computer industry in recession again.

1988
Cease-fire ends eight year Iran-Iraq war.

1989
Student protests for democracy in Tian'anmen Square, Beijing, China are violently

suppressed by the army.

Eastern bloc protests dismantle the Berlin Wall in Germany opening

the border between East and West Germany.

U.S. forces invade Panama and depose ruler, General Noriega.

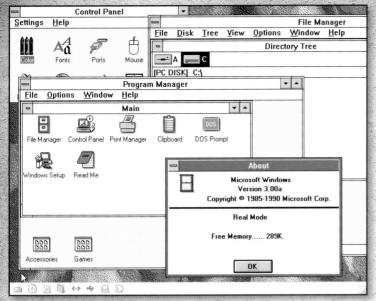

Windows 3.00a Screen Shot

Memory chip prices fell considerably. By '89, the number of fax (facsimile) machines in U.S. use had doubled from 1987 to 1.2 million.

Another boom was on in mobile radio telephones. More than 1 million U.S. customers were using them, spurring along a second generation of cellular phones using digital technology. Meanwhile, regulatory changes freed regional telephone companies to provide gateways to services such as Prodigy, offering news, weather, sports, financial and shopping information, and games, to PC users with modems.

ISDNs made their commercial debut in 1990, bringing the vision of a global voice, data, text, and video system closer to reality. ISDN boards for PCs permitted computer-to-computer communications, vastly extending the potential of networks. Wireless technology advances opened the prospect of individuals tapping into a global network with a pocket telephone. Cheaper and more portable cellular phones were feeding a burgeoning demand.

IBM raised the work stations ante in 1990 with machines able to do parallel processing. In software, Microsoft's Windows system blossomed and began to edge out MS/DOS as the industry standard operating system for PCs. Apple Computer sued Microsoft, claiming Windows had copied the "look and feel" of the Macintosh graphical interface.

The Hubble Space Telescope, a Lockheed Missiles & Space Company project, was launched into orbit, but proved to have a flaw that prevented its mirrors from focusing perfectly.

A nascent technology came on the commercial horizon as Conductus Inc. opened a Sunnyvale superconductor factory.

Two Stanford faculty stalwarts won 1990 Nobel Prizes. Canadian-born Richard E. Taylor shared the physics prize with Jerome Friedman and Henry Kendall for proving the existence of quarks in research at SLAC. Quarks, particles within positrons and neutrons, now are regarded as being among the fundamental building blocks of matter. Taylor worked at SLAC from 1962-68, and became a full Stanford professor in 1970. Emeritus Professor of Economics William F. Sharpe shared the economics prize for his capital asset pricing model, which led to the concept of "beta" in measuring portfolio risk. Sharpe's work is applied in stock investment and managing pension funds.

Hubble Space Telescope

1989
Exxon Valdez disaster off Alaska.

End of the Cold War.

1990
The U.S. creates virtual reality (computer simulation).

93 nations sign pact protecting the ozone layer.

South Africa frees Nelson Mandela after 27 years in prison. Apartheid begins to dismantle.

John Major succeeds British prime minister Margaret Thatcher.

In the late 1980s, Bing Yeh and his cofounder assembled a small team of engineers in a rented office on Apollo Way in Sunnyvale, Calif., to develop a new breed of nonvolatile memory technology—SuperFlash® for code or data storage in electronic systems and embedded memory for integrated logic circuits. Yeh had spent more than 10 years working at Intel, Honeywell, and Xicor before starting Silicon Storage Technology, Inc. (SST) in August 1989. In 1993 SST moved to its current headquarters on Sonora Court in Sunnyvale.

Nonvolatile memory devices retain data without a continuous supply of power. Virtually every microprocessor- or microcontroller-based electronic system requires nonvolatile memory to store program code consisting of a basic instruction set critical to the operation of the system. Prior to 1989, read-only memory (ROM), UV-light erasable PROM (EPROM), electrically erasable PROM (EEPROM), and the then-emerging FLASH memory created a succession of increasingly useful nonvolatile memory products for this purpose. However, these nonvolatile technologies either lack certain important functionality or are too expensive.

SST's new SuperFlash technology, because of its small-sector erase and fast reprogramming, did not have those deficiencies and was quickly adopted by the electronics industry after it introduced its first product in 1993. By the end of 1995, more than 90% of the PC motherboards produced in Taiwan had adopted SST's 1Mbit SuperFlash EEPROM product for the BIOS storage, thanks to SuperFlash's ability to provide the "plug-and-play" functionality needed for the just-introduced Windows 95 operating system. Riding on this success, SST went public on the NASDAQ market in November 1995.

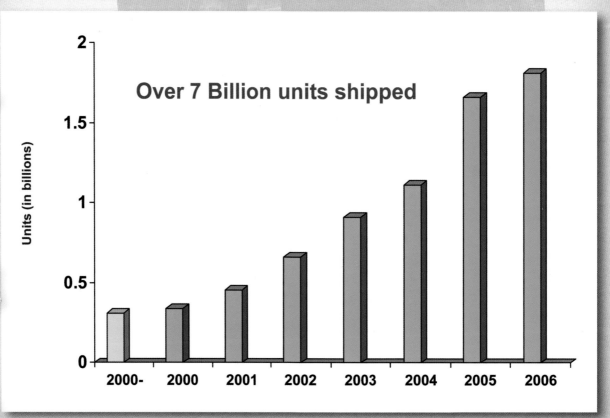

During the next 10 years, SST continued to work with its wafer foundry partners and technology licensees, including Sanyo, Seiko Epson, Samsung, and TSMC, to introduce a wide range of low- to medium density memory products and quickly expanded their applications beyond PCs. By the end of 2006, SST and its licensees had shipped more than seven billion integrated circuits based on SuperFlash technology. SST products are now used by almost every

Bing Yeh and co-founder in front of their first office located at 1208 Appollo Way in Sunnyvale, California.

major electronic system manufacturer and can be found in virtually every type of IT and consumer product. The applications of SuperFlash products include PCs, PDAs, hard disk drives, optical disk drives, printers, cellular phones, smart cards, GPS devices, digital TVs, MP3 players, DVD players, digital cameras and camcorders, video games, talking toys, electronic books, WiFi, cable/DSL modems, set-top boxes, Bluetooth modules, and many others.

In 2004, SST began a major initiative to transform itself from a pure play in flash to a more diversified company, with multiple product lines targeting the rapidly growing consumer and industrial products with embedded solid state data storage and RF wireless communication capabilities. Today, SST is the fifth largest NOR flash supplier in the world and is a major supplier of integrated circuits addressing the requirements of high-volume applications in the Internet computing, digital consumer, networking, and wireless communications markets.

30 MByte E2 Disk in 2.5" HDD form factor

5 MByte E2 Card in PCMCIA form factor

At the fall 1992 Comdex show, SST introduced the world's first single-board 30 MByte 2.5" solid state disk drive with standard ATA interface and a 5 MByte PCMCIA memory card with built-in controller and firmware. Before the show, typical notebook computer storage was a 2.5" hard disk drive with 20 MByte capacity. Because SST's solid state storage products were way ahead of their time, SST decided to focus on the memory component business after the 1992 Comdex show.

Jen-Hsun Huang, Co-Founder
President, and CEO, NVIDIA

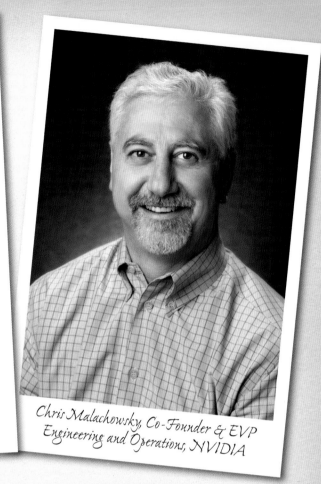

Chris Malachowsky, Co-Founder & EVP
Engineering and Operations, NVIDIA

NVIDIA was founded in 1993 by Jen-Hsun Huang, Chris Malachowsky, and Curtis Priem. The three met while Jen-Hsun was at LSI Logic and Chris and Curtis were at Sun Microsystems. In typical Silicon Valley start-up fashion, the trio held brainstorming meetings at a Denny's restaurant in San Jose and started the company with a single PC in the living room of Curtis' condominium in Fremont.

From the beginning, NVIDIA reflected the founders' passion for graphics. Looking back at the early days, CEO Jen-Hsun Huang commented: "We believed the 3D graphics industry was special because there was a lot of room for innovation. The technology had nearly infinite headroom." The founders saw an opportunity to take technology that had been dedicated to flight simulators and scientific computing and apply it to everyday PCs.

NVIDIA's initial product, NV1, was an ambitious attempt to bring multimedia functionality (graphics, video, and sound) to the Win386 PC at a time when PCs were focused on office tasks such as spreadsheets and word processing. Ahead of its time, the revolutionary NV1 did not achieve market success. However, the process of developing NV1 formed the "DNA" for which NVIDIA would become known: a continual pushing of technology boundaries combined with relentless execution and a propensity for risk-taking.

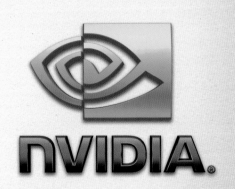

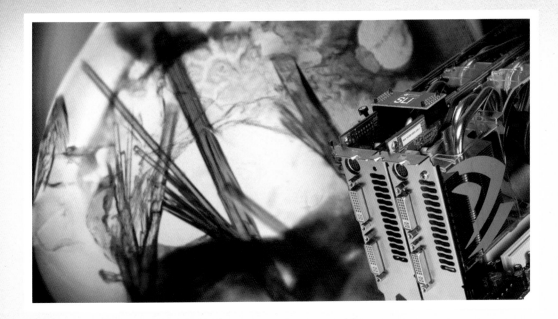

In 1997, NVIDIA introduced the RIVA 128. An industry breakthrough, it became NVIDIA's first commercial success and created a new product category—the GPU, or graphics processing unit. The GPU set new standards for PC graphics and transformed the world of 3D gaming (the first popular application of graphics on the PC). Over the next few years, NVIDIA's team of inventors pushed the original GPU a step further with the notion of "real-time programmable shading," which put the processing power of the GPU into the hands of 3D content developers around the world, providing them with an infinite palette of tools for creating better, more realistic graphics.

Today, fourteen years after its founding, NVIDIA is the world leader in computer graphics technologies. NVIDIA products power the visual experience on a variety of innovative, market-leading platforms, from the Sony PlayStation 3 game console to sophisticated workstations tasked with solving the world's hardest problems. As a notable point of comparison, the first NVIDIA GPU contained four million transistors. Today's GPU is approaching one billion.

At its core, NVIDIA is driven by a culture of innovation and a desire to build products that transform industries. As Jen-Hsun Huang says: "At NVIDIA, we don't build things that our competitors are building; we build things we believe the world will need. I absolutely believe that this passion for innovation will drive our long-term success and our relevance to the world."

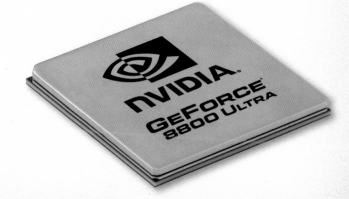

Since it was incorporated in 1990, Los Altos, California–based Rambus Inc. has been providing leading chip and system companies with memory architectures and interface solutions that solve some of the most challenging bandwidth problems. Rambus's leadership and industry-standard products enable state-of-the-art performance from PCs, video game consoles, digital TVs, set-top boxes, and mobile phones.

Rambus was born as the result of a revelation by company co-founder and acclaimed idea man Michael Farmwald. During the 1980s, when he worked at MIPS Technologies, Farmwald got caught up in the challenge of how to make computer memory work faster. He saw that memory data transmission rates were very slow compared to the processing efficiency of other logic circuits and that, to compensate for their slowness, memory chips had to run in parallel, which made costs high. He wanted to find a better solution.

Michael Farmwald, Founder

Mark Horowitz, Founder

That solution soon came to him—high-speed memory was needed as well as a high-speed bus. To increase memory speed, a packet-based synchronous interface would be required—standing the terminals at one end of the package would shorten the transmission path. So Farmwald devised a system to make that happen.

Before that time, Farmwald had come up with several other great ideas—but he had never been able to bring any to fruition. This time things were different. He continued to develop his idea, knowing that high-speed memory circuits would be an "absolute hit" and in great demand. But he also knew that designing circuits wasn't his forte. He decided he needed a partner and he found that partner in Mark Horowitz, a renowned integrated circuit designer and professor at Stanford University.

Horowitz, however, had no interest in starting a

business. More than that, when Farmwald showed him his idea, Horowitz said it wouldn't work. He pointed out mistake after mistake, until Farmwald thought all was lost. Still, Horowitz eventually encouraged Farmwald by saying he found the idea interesting and the technology fascinating and, finally, became convinced that Farmwald's idea had great possibilities. The two men agreed to launch a business venture together.

With their business idea in place, the two co-founders next needed to raise capital to get underway. They were introduced to venture capitalist Bill Davidow, who couldn't believe what he heard—that Rambus memory technology would provide data-transfer speeds 10 to 20 times faster than those of then-existing memory chips. But Farmwald and Horowitz convinced him—and when they mentioned they planned to license their DRAM (dynamic random access memory) technology rather than manufacture products, Davidow invested $600,000 in the burgeoning enterprise. Eventually Rambus secured $1.8 million from three venture capitalists.

But being able to produce DRAM products wasn't going to be enough—the entrepreneurs needed a microprocessor that would be able to work with high-speed memory. Davidow suggested that Intel's microprocessor be the microprocessor of choice and helped the founders gain the cooperation of Intel co-founder Gordon Moore.

Rambus went into operation in a corner of Davidow's office, and Davidow, Farmwald, and Horowitz set out to reach licensing agreements with major manufacturers. But no American or European company would come onboard—each manufacturer, even Intel, said it would only be interested if other manufacturers decided first to go with this new technology. When Davidow approached Japanese manufacturers, though, the answer was different. Several businesses were immediately interested, and Toshiba soon made the leap. It became the first major manufacturer of the Rambus DRAM (RDRAM), followed soon by Fujitsu and NEC.

In early 1991, Intel, which had decided to cooperate on producing the prototype, announced that the device was ready for testing. When the power was turned on, a cheer went up in the lab. The prototype worked, showing that a data transfer speed of 500 megabits per second was possible.

While it appeared that the positive test would be Rambus's key to success, most equipment manufacturers at the time didn't yet require RDRAM's high data transfer rate, and the company was not instantly flooded with orders. Still, design and development of RDRAM went on at Toshiba, as well as at Fujitsu and NEC. In early 1992, Toshiba completed the prototype of a 4.5Mb RDRAM, with an amazing data-transmission speed.

32 bit RIMM

Rambus engineers innovate in the area of high-speed interface design.

Finally, equipment manufacturers that had previously backed away started to find the new technology interesting. Rambus's big break came when Nintendo's Genyo Takeda saw—and was amazed by—a 4.5Mb RDRAM installed in a Silicon Graphics (SGI) workstation. Takeda wanted RDRAM to power the next generation of Nintendo's computer games, but a design change would have to be made—a two-layer printed circuit board was desired, rather than the four-layer board RDRAM was designed for. After months of work to overcome associated design challenges, Rambus engineers developed a successful pilot of a two-layer board, and Nintendo was finally ready to proceed.

In addition, both Toshiba and NEC were able to supply both Nintendo and SGI with powerful, reliable 250Mb RDRAM memory chips. When that happened, a number of other equipment manufacturers, including Intel, signed license agreements with Rambus. NEC subsequently shipped more than 50 million RDRAM chips, and once Toshiba began production of the next-generation RDRAMs, that company, too, became a successful Rambus partner. Following the launch of the Nintendo64 game console, the Rambus co-founders' great idea made an impact in the marketplace in the Sony PlayStation®2. To date, over 110 million PS2s have been sold, and Rambus's next-generation memory solution, the XDR™ memory architecture, along with its high-speed parallel bus technology FlexIO™, now helps Sony's PlayStation3 deliver real-world graphics to consumers.

Rambus continues to design and deliver the world's fastest memory architectures to enable state-of-the-art consumer and compute platforms. First introduced in 2001, Rambus's XDR memory architecture is the world's fastest, providing dramatically higher performance than today's standard memories.

The XDR memory architecture features key enabling technologies built on patented Rambus innovations that include low-voltage, low-power Differential Rambus Signaling Level (DRSL); Octal Data Rate (ODR) technology that transfers eight bits of data each clock cycle; FlexPhase™ circuit technology for precise on-chip alignment of data with clock; and Dynamic-Point-to-Point (DPP) for both enhanced signal integrity and scalability.

To extend its vibrant history of technology innovation, Rambus continues to invest heavily in high-speed interface technology, focusing on advanced circuit design, logic architecture, system engineering, signal integrity, verification, and testing. By using a multidisciplinary approach, Rambus engineers identify system bottlenecks and develop the technologies required for faster signaling and advance system designs. Their innovations have resulted in more than 1,000 issued and pending patents.

A great deal of Rambus's success is also the result of holding true to the founders' mission: to continuously enrich the end user's experience with electronic devices. The company also believes strongly in strengthening and improving the quality of life in the community in which it's located, and does so through grants and by working with community partners. Rambus invests in education through such opportunities as math,

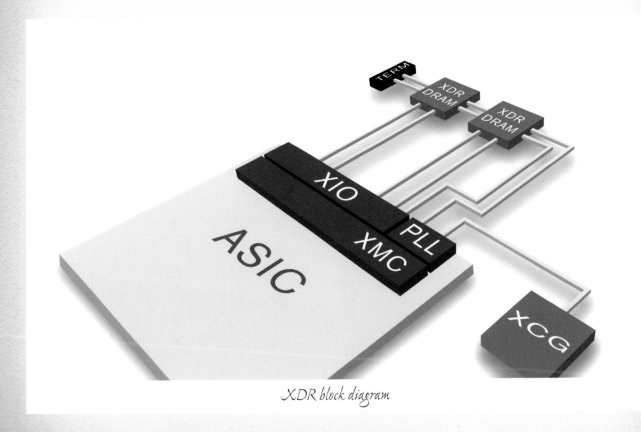

XDR block diagram

Rambus headquarters in Los Altos, California.

science, and technology programs that target low-income areas and encourage the gifted innovators of tomorrow. The company also donates hardware and software and provides training and support to a number of academic institutions. To meet other community needs, Rambus invests in employee-recommended agencies such as Second Harvest Food Bank and the Boys and Girls Clubs of America.

While it took some time for Rambus to become the company its co-founders envisioned, today it is one of the world's premier technology licensing companies focused on high-performance memory architectures, licensing its patents and products to customers in North America, Asia, and Europe. With Harold Hughes as president and CEO and with co-founders Mike Farmwald and Mark Horowitz serving as senior technical advisor and chief scientist, respectively, Rambus continues to deliver greater performance and speed for a broad range of consumer, computing, and communications systems.

Asus motherboard with Rambus components

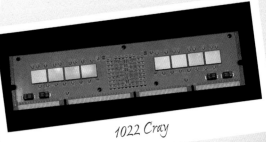

1022 Cray

You've got an idea that you think society needs. Your friends and family discourage you, but you go ahead. With a small amount of money and everything you can beg or get on credit, you start your enterprise. After a lot of hard work, and good, bad, and unexpected experiences—you fail; you lose your money, your dream, other people's dreams that you inspired and, of course, other people's money. What now?

In Silicon Valley, you accept the loss and start over.

"There's just social acceptance of failure in this climate. And without an acceptance of failure, you have a concomitant level of acceptance for risk. So you have to be able to fail in order to take a risk. If you die when you fall down skiing, not many people are going to take up skiing. And so if you commit social suicide by starting a company that fails, not very many companies start, and so you find that the people that have the education and the standing in those societies don't take the risk."

> — **Nolan Bushnell**
> **Founder, Atari Corporation**

In the Silicon Valley culture, risk is exalted.

"The glory of life is that you can fail, and you cannot fail if you try hard."

> — **Barney Oliver**
> **Former Director of Research, Hewlett-Packard**

"There's no good time to start your own company. No matter when you pick the time, it's always going to be risky. So I decided that, what the heck, I would do it. If worse comes to worse and I fail, I'll go back and get a job."

> — **David Lam**
> **Founder of Lam Research**

"You have to create opportunity for people to fail safely, because no one can have a 100% success."

> — **Alejandro Zaffaroni,**
> **Founder, Syntex, ALZA, and Affymax**

"People said we were crazy. What kept us going was probably several things. Perhaps one of the key ones was the camaraderie that you immediately form with this small group of founders because you're stuck in the situation and you've got to prove it to each other."

> — **James Hobart**
> **Founder, Coherent**

"Risk-taking has become almost celebrated in Silicon Valley, and entrepreneurship has become celebrated. The most sought-after positions are often in small firms or in startups, which is very different from the rest of the country. People in Silicon Valley recognize that you may learn from failure, and in fact, there's an important element of learning about technology, about organization, about many things through the process of failure. You have many people in Silicon Valley who have started multiple companies. They fail, and then they start right back up again."

> — **Annalee Saxenian**
> **Author, *Regional Advantage***

"Some of the failures are as widely discussed as the successes. And even in the failures, people are admired for trying. You've got to act, and you've got to be willing to fail. You've got to be willing to crash and burn. If you're afraid of failing, you won't get very far."

> — **Steve Jobs**
> **Founder, Apple Computer and NeXT**

"Nothing venture, nothing win."

> — **Sir William S. Gilbert**
> **The Mikado**

Chapter 16: Morphing, Downsizing, and Restructuring

Terminator 2: Judgment Day, 1991's hit movie, opened the public's eyes to a new era of digital imaging and special effects that was being born in Silicon Valley and the regional multimedia community. Through morphing, a technique employed by George Lucas' Industrial Light and Magic company, the film's "bad guy" came out of the floor and changed shapes at will. Although the digitizing behind morphing took costly special computer equipment to accomplish, the era it introduced was to lead to CD-ROMs on many home computers and inexpensive programs for putting photos on disk and manipulating them.

Progress and pain both marked the Valley's 1991-92 period. Total jobs in Santa Clara County declined by 25,000 as defense companies downsized and large high-technology companies restructured. However, real wages, exports, and venture capital all gained. The U.S. pulled even with Japan in semiconductor sales in 1992—a prelude to forging ahead.

Silicon Valley ranked as a global leader in integrated circuits, microprocessors, personal computers, CD-ROMs, networking, and three-dimensional imaging. Software became the region's fastest-growing job generator.

The Valley also mulled a new initiative—the idea of creating a Joint Venture: Silicon Valley Network that would function as a coordinating body to bring together industry and civic figures to make the area more receptive to industries' needs and more collaborative in meeting its governmental needs.

In 1991, several companies introduced wireless local area network systems (LANs). Using nondirectional microwave technology, unlike old systems that had to be beamed at a specific target, LANs could handle data transmission speeds similar to those used for existing wire installations.

A trend was running toward lightweight notebook computers, including 5-pound laptops such as Apple's model. Although the year was turbulent, the computer industry recession appeared to have ended.

AT&T divested itself of 19 million shares of Sun Microsystems Inc. stock at a profit exceeding $200 million. The move was related to AT&T's hostile takeover of NCR Corporation, which became its networked computing resource.

The Soviet Union and its Communist Party collapsed completely in 1991, alleviating fears that a crisis might somehow bring on nuclear warfare. But in a new "post-Cold War" era, no one could clearly see what was coming. In the Persian Gulf, a U.S.-led coalition of countries gave Iraq a stunning "high tech" defeat after Iraq invaded and annexed Kuwait.

Apple Newton

In 1992, a court decision opened the way for "Baby Bells" (regional telephone operating systems once part of AT&T) to offer home computer users electronic *Yellow Pages* in the short run and, later, on-line interactive video. This step was one of a number leading to the often-predicted convergence of computers, telecommunications, and cable TV. Industry analysts foresaw each field competing for the others' customers.

Novelties on the '92 cheaper-and-lighter computing front included Apple's pocket-sized Newton, an executive organizer with built-in wireless communications, and notebooks with an electronic pen replacing the keyboard. For the most part, the pen systems ultimately flopped.

Silicon Graphics acquired MIPS Computers in 1992 when a financial crisis beset that company. MIPS

1991

U.S.-led allies liberate Kuwait in 100 hours.

Lithuanian voters overwhelmingly back independence.

Strategic Arms Reduction Treaty signed at Moscow summit.

Soviet President Mikhail Gorbachev survived a coup attempt.

United Nations welcomes seven new members, including North and South Korea.

Islamic Jihad releases Terry Anderson, U.S. newsman held for 2,455 days.

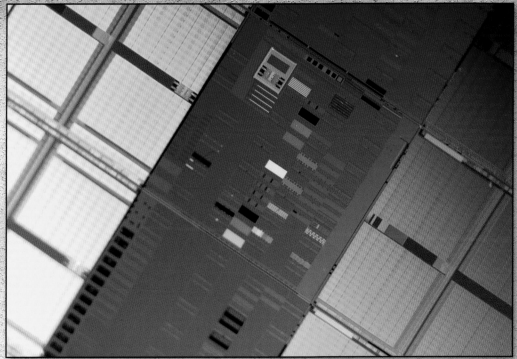

300mm silicon test wafer made using Intel's leading 45nm process technology.

continued to operate as a unit of Silicon Graphics, building the powerful computers that run its 3-D graphics. The two companies had collaborated closely in past years.

Compression Labs, Inc. (CLI), market leader in videoconferencing technologies and systems, in 1992 introduced the VideoPhone 2500, which CLI worked with AT&T to develop. Compression technology was opening the way for display of video clips on computers and other advances. Multimedia—shorthand for the addition of fine audio and video capabilities to standard computer attributes—was on the way to becoming a standard feature of "loaded" PCs.

At last responding to the demands of consumers and corporate data processing managers, a computer industry consortium formed, promising to make all workstation computers run the same open operating system, thereby freeing customers to buy any supplier's software. However, "middleman" programs designed to run between the software and the operating system emerged, relieving some of the open-systems pressure.

The U.S. government began a move to create nationwide "superhighways for data," an outgrowth of legislation proposed by Senator Al Gore Jr. to speed up an existing network. High speeds were needed to link supercomputers and, via the Internet, make their power available to smaller universities, libraries, and government research centers.

New on the semiconductor front were 8-inch silicon wafers, produced in an Intel fab in Santa Clara. New advances in manufacturing technology had enabled this step toward increased efficiency. In 1991, meanwhile, Intel had ceased further development of the EPROM in favor of flash memory development. Flash memory chips retain data even when computer system power is turned off.

Richard Robert Ernst won the 1991 Nobel Prize for chemistry for broadening the usefulness of high-resolution nuclear magnetic resonance (NMR) spectroscopy. Ernst, a Swiss professor, had spent five years as a research scientist at Varian Associates in Palo Alto where, with U.S. colleague Weston A. Anderson, he made one of the discoveries cited for his award. His work built upon earlier studies by Stanford's Felix Bloch, a 1952 Nobelist. Until Ernst's refinements, NMR had been a tool for chemistry; after his refinements, it served also in physics, biology, and medicine.

Biotechnology firms, once clustered mainly near San Francisco and Berkeley, had spread in large numbers to central Silicon Valley. Venture capital firms were investing heavily in them.

1991
Gorbachev resigns, saying Soviet Union no longer exists.

1992
China tests large nuclear device.

U.S. President George Bush and Russian Pres. Boris Yeltsin declare end of Cold War.

North and South Korea sign pacts aimed at reunification.

Panamanian strongman Noriega sentenced to 40 years in prison.

Atrocities prompt UN to declare Yugoslavia's seat vacant.

Chapter 17: Surfing on the Internet

SGI Workstations

The Internet caught the public's fancy in 1993-94. Originally noncommercial in nature and without much funding or central management, it was simply a linkup of diverse computer networks based at academic or research centers. Then software companies introduced products to make the Internet easier to use, on-line services opened gateways into it, and personal computer users became able to sign on.

As people began to grasp the Internet's possibilities—spurred by a Washington champion, Vice President Al Gore—the user count expanded phenomenally. Intrigued by all the activities they could carry on in cyberspace, computer buffs spent hours exploring the Net just for fun.

Jim Clark, founder of Silicon Graphics and Netscape voiced the wonder of it: "The Internet is the de facto standard communications network. We think of it today as a data communications network, but voice is data, video is data, images are data, text are data- all of these things are just data-and so the Internet is going to be the super highway that we all have been looking for."

Although companies in many parts of North America, Europe, and Asia were racing to capitalize on the Internet, a good deal of the activity was concentrated in Silicon Valley in companies large and small. Installations of fiberoptic cables, high-speed switches, and wireless transmitters were in progress around the San Francisco Bay, and Cupertino and Palo Alto were among the cities gaining an early place on the Net. Smart Valley, a Palo Alto-based nonprofit consortium, aimed to spur development of a regional infrastructure in order to revitalize education, reduce health care costs, create jobs, and make local government more responsive.

In 1993, ultrasmall computing systems equipped with wireless networking systems came into vogue. Both they and home and office computers were offered the promise of networking with other computers on a data superhighway.

At the movies, meanwhile, fans' eyes were popping. Silicon Graphics' 3-D imaging was behind many of the extraordinary technical effects that seemed to bring prehistoric animals to life in Steven Spielberg's 1993 movie, *Jurassic Park*, a box office record-setter. Then came *Forrest Gump*, with scenes of its slow-witted hero in action with dead presidents John F. Kennedy and Lyndon B. Johnson.

Scene from the 1994 movie The Mask

The same year saw the debut of a new product promoting connections between PC users: PCMCIA cards. Named for its designer, the Personal Computer Memory Card Industry Association, the device, about the size of a business card, but thicker, could be inserted in a slot in a pocket-size computer to give it special functions such as extra memory.

Handheld personal digital assistants—PDAs—also bowed in. The palm-size computers had no keyboards; instead, users wrote on a plastic grid with a special pen. There was no standard operating system, and a consortium called General Magic formed to try to develop the proper software.

Two computer giants' marketplace skids led to ousters of John Sculley at Apple Computer and John Akers at IBM. At NExT Computer, Steve Jobs decided to focus on software and quit hardware. Borland International of Scotts

1993
Czechoslovakia splits into Czech Republic and Slovakia.

Waco standoff ends in tragedy.

Danish voters narrowly approve union with Europe.

The Vatican and Israel reach an accord.

The World Wide Web was born at CERN.

1994
Disastrous earthquake devastates Los Angeles suburbs.

- 142 -

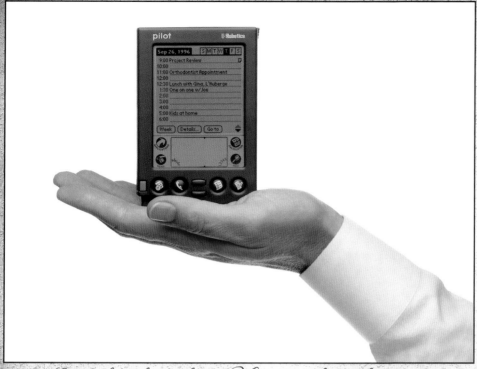

Original Palm Pilot PDA (personal digital assistant)

Valley, once seen as a major PC software player, entered deep decline.

A new Cray Y-MP C90 supercomputer—the world's fastest—was added to Ames Research Center's NAS (Numerical Aerodynamic Simulation) program equipment. It upped Ames's computing power more than sixfold. The C90 can do more than 6 billion calculations per second, and can hold 1 billion words in memory.

Space shuttle Endeavour's crew successfully repaired the Hubble Space Telescope in orbit. Many rated the fix-it mission NASA's biggest test since the 1969 moon landings.

On July 1, 1994, the Navy disestablished Moffett Field Naval Air Station, and NASA's Ames Research Center began managing the facility as Moffett Federal Base. Since 1987, Ames had operated its 14th wind tunnel—the largest wind tunnel on earth for aerodynamic testing.

Computer and telecommunications firms were converging, as evidenced by AT&T bidding to merge with McCaw Cellular, the largest U.S. independent cellular company, and Bell Atlantic seeking to buy cable television conglomerate TCI, Inc., so as to use TCI lines outside its own service area to carry telephone calls. (The Bell Atlantic-TCI deal later fell through.) Cable TV companies could compete with telephone companies, which in turn wanted to enter the cable TV business to finance laying of fiber optic cable to homes.

Intel Corp. in 1993 unveiled its fifth-generation microprocessor, the Pentium, packing 3.1 million transistors and capable of executing more than 1 million instructions per second (MIPS). Motorola brought out a rival chip family, the PowerPC microprocessors, developed jointly in conjunction with IBM Corp. and Apple Computer.

Late in '94, the Internet became the medium carrying harsh consumer criticism of Intel for its reluctance to replace Pentiums after a flaw affecting complicated division problems was revealed. At length the company bowed to public opinion and offered a replacement to any owner who asked for it, at a cost estimated at $475 million.

In early 1995 Intel and Advanced Micro Devices settled their legal battle, begun in 1987 after Intel declined to share its 386 microprocessor technology with AMD, which then cloned the chip. During the litigation, Intel had brought out its i486 and the Pentium; AMD had brought out a 486 and was at work on K-5, a fifth-generation microprocessor of its own design.

Hubble Telescope

NXP Semiconductors, formerly Philips Semiconductors, has a deep and diverse history in Silicon Valley. That history began with Signetics, which became Philips Semiconductors in 1993 and then NXP in 2006, when parent company Philips Electronics sold its semiconductor division to a consortium of private equity firms.

Signetics was the first company in the world to be established for the exclusive purpose of developing, manufacturing, and distributing integrated circuits (ICs). Today, NXP creates semiconductors, system solutions, and software that deliver better sensory experiences to consumers using mobile phones, personal media players, TVs, set-top boxes, identification applications, in-car entertainment, and a wide range of other electronic devices and systems.

Nexperia 5210 system solution for cellular phones allows devices to be used at home, over fixed-line broadband networks and outside via a cellular network.

Signetics was formed in September 1961 by a group of scientists and engineers working at Fairchild Semiconductor. David Allison, David James, Lionel Kattner, and Mark Weisenstern were among the early pioneers of IC technology. Like Fairchild's founders before them, and generations of entrepreneurs to come, they struck out on their own, calling their new company Signetics, a contraction of "signal network ICs." Signetics was an early innovator in digital logic, with many of its logic circuits becoming industry standards. Within a year of the company's founding, its first family of bipolar digital diode transistor logic circuits gained market acceptance and found initial application in military and space systems. Among the company's early innovations were the 555 timer, Dolby circuits, and the programmable read-only memory.

In November of 1962, Corning Glass Works purchased a majority interest in Signetics. For

The world's first video postprocessor IC with Motion Accurate Picture Processing (MAPP). This processor drastically improves high definition video on LCD TVs.

the next few years, all company operations, including manufacturing, R&D, and administration, were carried out in Sunnyvale, California. However, by the mid-1960s, the need to increase production levels compelled the company to establish its first off-site plant. Signetics became the first IC company to receive both Minuteman approval, in 1967, and NASA line certification, in 1970.

In the early 1970s, then-company president Charles Harwood initiated a revolutionary quality program, which was followed in 1985 by a "zero defects" warranty on all Signetics products—Signetics was the first IC company to offer such a warranty. That program, still actively implemented within NXP, has become an industry model.

By the mid-1970s, Signetics had become a broad-based supplier of its major IC product lines and went public for a short while, from 1973 to 1975. In June 1975 the company was purchased by U.S. Philips Corporation, a wholly owned subsidiary of N.V. Philips of the Netherlands. Philips Semiconductors then extended its base in Silicon Valley by acquiring VLSI Technologies, an ASIC semiconductor company, in 1999. In 2001 the company transferred all Silicon Valley–based activities to its campus in San Jose.

NXP Semiconductors now employs more than 1,700 people in North America in four main locations: San Jose, California; Tempe, Arizona; Austin, Texas; and Fishkill, New York. San Jose is currently home to the company's North America Sales Force and two of its many business groups: the connectivity business group and the standard products IC group. The Fishkill facility is a U.S.-based fabricator, producing high-quality semiconductors for a broad range of consumer and mobile phone applications.

Chapter 18: A Vintage Year in Silicon Valley

For most of Silicon Valley, 1995 was a vintage year, perhaps the best ever. Booming sales of computers, chips, and semiconductor equipment sent technology stocks surging in the first half of the year. By the three-quarters mark, the science and technology mutual funds index was up 46.7%, and a number of the larger companies had registered market-value increases of near 100% — some 200% or more. Barring anything like the October 1987 crash, 1995 promised to end with many record gains.

Amazingly fast growth occurred in much of Silicon Valley industry. Demand ran high for computers and peripherals, semiconductors, semiconductor manufacturing equipment, communications devices, and multimedia products. Biotechnology did not generally share in the boom. Venture capital firms were active. Companies bought land, erected buildings and hired again after a long no-growth period. Seeking to cash in on the Internet's popularity, online, database, computer, networking, telephone, and cable television companies were all scrambling for position.

Technology advanced rapidly, too, spurring intense competition in some arenas. In disk drives, for example, new product generations lasted only nine months, prices fell 12% each quarter, and companies had to increase the storage capacity on a disk 60% a year to keep pace with their rivals. Large hard disks commonly stored 1.6 gigabytes, more than 50 times as much data as a decade earlier.

This pace forced one major consolidation. Seagate Technology Inc. agreed to acquire Conner Peripherals. The purchase of the No. 3 disk-drive company by the No. 2 company would create one company with $7.5 billion in revenues.

Hard Disk Drives

The hottest initial public offering turned out to be Netscape Communications Corp., a Mountain View firm founded by James H. Clark, who earlier founded Silicon Graphics, Inc. The stock more than tripled before settling back a bit, but wild action on the initial public offering signaled keen interest in simple ways to access — and do business on — the Internet.

In computer networking, acquisitions and mergers were rife. Three growing companies, each already well past $1 billion in revenues, appeared locked in a battle for dominance. Out in front were Cisco Systems of San Jose and 3Com of Santa Clara, which made its 11th acquisition in four years (not counting putting its name on the San Francisco stadium formerly known as Candlestiek Park). Also in the derby was Bay Networks, formed of a recent merger of

1995
GOP takes control of Congress, led by Bob Dole, Newt Gingrich.

Oklahoma City courthouse bomb kills 168.

Chicago heat wave kills 450.

Affirmative action ended by UC Regents.

Belarus shoots down 2 U.S. balloonists.

U.S. reopens diplomacy with Hanoi.

Jury acquits O.J. Simpson of murders.

- 146 -

Intel Pentium Processor

SynOptics of Santa Clara and Wellfleet of Massachusetts.

In software, introduction of Microsoft's Windows 95 operating system took the spotlight in August. But before that, Microsoft — under pressure from the Justice Department — dropped its bid to make a $2 billion purchase of Intuit Inc., the maker of the popular Quicken and TurboTax personal finance programs. Intuit employees in Menlo Park reportedly cheered when the deal collapsed. Oracle Corporation, Silicon Valley's largest software company, had its eye on the Internet, and so did Adobe Systems.

In microprocessors, Intel pressed its hot-selling Pentium advantage while rivals such as AMD, Nexgen and Cyrix aimed for faster superchips in hopes of reducing Intel's lead. Apple, IBM, and Motorola teamed up to bring out PowerPC chips using RISC architecture, somewhat faster than the Pentium but possibly not enough to peel off market share.

In the workstations market, Sun Microsystems brought out the 64-bit Ultrasparc, the first major revamping of its Sparc architecture since 1987, claiming unique multimedia features. Hewlett-Packard, Digital Equipment Company, and Intel with its projected P6 were working on faster-rated workstation chips for future introduction. MIPS Technologies, a Silicon Graphics subsidiary, had fielded its R10000 processor, "the fastest yet." Pyramid Technology was grouping MIPS and other chips in what Pyramid called "the most robust massively parallel offering."

Imagine testing a nuclear weapon with a computer. The U.S. Department of Energy announced a contract for Intel to develop a supercomputer using 9,000 P6 processors that would be capable of simulating nuclear weapons tests — without the fallout.

In the shrinking U.S. defense industry, Lockheed and Martin Marietta completed their $10 billion merger as Lockheed Martin Corp. When worker layoff plans were announced, Lockheed Missiles & Space Company in Sunnyvale — already down from a peak of nearly 25,000 employees to 11,000 — escaped major cuts, indicating its projects would continue little changed in the near term. At adjoining Moffett Federal Base, a struggle was on to repel proposals to reduce Ames Research Center's role within NASA.

Driven by the desire to avoid a rerun of the VHS-Beta war of decades past, global companies planning to manufacture digital video disks compromised on a single standard. A group of seven manufacturers led by Toshiba Corp. accepted a proposal from the other camp, led by Philips Electronics and Sony Corp. Alan Bell, a specialist in CD technology at IBM's Almaden Research Center in San Jose headed a computer industry workgroup, including representatives of Apple, HP, Sun, and other companies, that successfully urged a single CD technology that would meet their needs.

The new disk would store a 133-minute movie at the highest audio and video quality, or store audio and computer data and software. It would have more than seven times a CD-ROM's computer data capacity. The *New York Times* said the process behind the agreement reflected the convergence of the consumer electronics, computer, and entertainment industries as a single multimedia industry.

Another ballyhooed form of convergence, that of computers and telecommunications, was cast into doubt when AT&T abandoned its costly vision of operating as a single corporate empire and divided itself into three companies.

| U.S. stocks soar; Dow breaks 5,000. | Budget tussle shuts down U.S. government. | Pixar IPO nets Steve Jobs a paper billion. | Japan makes apology for World War II. | Papers run Unabomber's manifesto. | Clinton OKs closing of 105 military bases. | U.S.-Russian space linkup first in 20 years. |

eadquartered in the heart of Silicon Valley, Communications & Power Industries (CPI) is a global leader in the development, manufacturing, and distribution of a wide range of products that generate, amplify, and transmit high-power/high-frequency microwave and radio frequency (RF) signals. By producing these crucial products, used in a wide variety of applications, CPI has fulfilled its founders' plans to develop a forward-looking, diversified enterprise to "conduct research in the fields of physical science of every kind or nature."

Those founders were Russell and Sigurd Varian, who started Varian Associates in 1948 and introduced the klystron, a specialized vacuum electron device, as their first commercial product. Initially Varian Associates' Electron Device Business, in 1995 this group became Communications & Power Industries, Inc., which is now an industry powerhouse in its own right, building on its great heritage of technology, leadership, product, and manufacturing excellence. CPI currently is comprised of six operating divisions: Microwave Power Products (Palo Alto, Calif.), Beverly Microwave (Beverly, Mass.), Satcom (Ontario, Canada), Communications & Medical Products (Ontario, Canada), Malibu (Camarillo, Calif.), and Econco (Woodland, Calif.), which together provide products to serve six end markets.

CPI is a preferred provider of state-of-the-art vacuum electron devices, such as the high-power klystron shown here, that are used in scientific applications, including in accelerators for nuclear, particle and high-energy physics programs.

For the radar market, CPI supplies products used in a variety of military systems, including search, fire control, tracking, and weather. These products include microwave and power grid sources, microwave amplifiers, and complete transmitter subsystems, and are used in airborne, ground-based, and shipboard radar systems. CPI has a sole-provider position in numerous landmark radar programs.

CPI also is a leading supplier of products to the electronic warfare market. These products protect ships, aircraft, and land targets against radar-guided weapons. CPI products protect high-value assets by enabling the jamming or deception of radar signals generated by enemy systems.

In the medical market, CPI focuses on diagnostic and treatment applications. Diagnostic products include X-ray generators, software and user interfaces, and operator consoles for

CPI offers unique, state-of-the-art facilities for the development and production of large microwave devices.

diagnostic imaging. For treatment applications CPI provides x-ray generators and klystron vacuum electron devices, which provide the microwave energy to accelerate a beam of energy toward a cancerous tumor, for high-end radiation therapy machines.

CPI divides the communications market into satellite, terrestrial broadcast, and over-the-horizon applications. Its satellite amplifiers meet nearly every frequency and power need of both fixed and mobile satellite communications in the military and commercial arenas. Its terrestrial broadcast products serve the AM, FM, and shortwave radio markets plus the VHF and UHF TV markets. Its over-the-horizon microwave-based systems transmit voice, data and video signals over several hundred miles.

CPI remains a consistently high-quality manufacturer by implementing modern manufacturing methodologies.

In the industrial arena, CPI provides a number of specialized product lines for systems used for material processing, instrumentation, and RF signal generation. In the scientific market CPI products are used in reactor fusion programs and accelerators for the study of high-energy particle physics.

In addition to its strong presence in defense applications, CPI has made its mark in the commercial application field. To continue to help customers drive strategic advances in both of these areas, CPI will continue to develop superior high-power, broader-bandwidth, and higher-frequency microwave products.

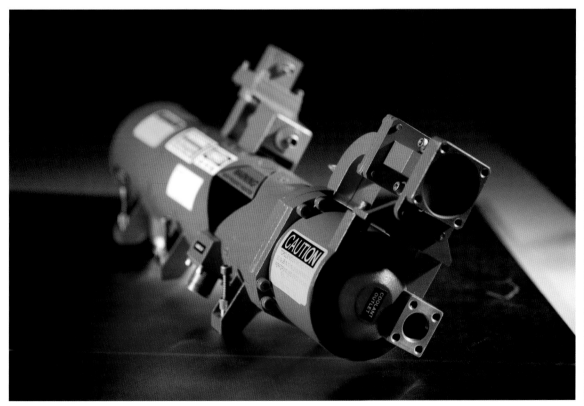

CPI products, including the coupled cavity TWT shown here, are used in numerous radar applications.

In the short time since Yahoo! Inc. went public, in 1996, this leading global Internet communications, commerce, and media company's rise has been nothing short of meteoric. But its early growth, from personal Internet interest list to widely used directory for locating useful Websites, was meteoric as well. In February 1994, Yahoo! co-founders and then-Ph.D. candidates David Filo and Jerry Yang started "Jerry and David's Guide to the World Wide Web" as a way to keep track of their favorite Internet sites. By the fall of that year, word of their hierarchical list of links had spread well beyond their Stanford University trailer and Yahoo! experienced its first one-million-hit day, which translated to being visited by nearly 100,000 users.

Filo and Yang quickly realized that the little online guide they had put together could readily be turned into a useful business. Calling their creation Yahoo!, because the two liked the word's meaning of "rude, unsophisticated, uncouth"—though some say Yahoo is an acronym for "Yet Another Hierarchical Officious Oracle"—they secured venture capital and hired an expert management team: Tim Koogle, an experienced Stanford Engineering Department graduate and Motorola veteran, and Jeffrey Mallett, who had founded Novell's WordPerfect consumer division. With 49 employees, Yahoo!—the exclamation mark was added because the word Yahoo had already been trademarked—was launched in a highly successful IPO.

During the late 1990s, Yahoo! diversified from Web directory to Web portal, to provide eager users with many more services. The business acquired such companies as online communications group Four11, whose Web mail service Rocketmail became Yahoo! Mail; ClassicGames.com, which was turned into Yahoo! Games; direct marketing company Yoyodyne; Web hosting provider GeoCities; and eGroups, which became Yahoo! Groups. Yahoo! also launched Yahoo! Messenger at the end of the decade.

Yahoo! Inc. Headquarters in Sunnyvale, California

After surviving the dot-com bubble burst, Yahoo! continued to expand its services even further. It acquired several additional search engines, including Inktomi and AltaVista, and today its technology provides one of the largest search engines on the Web. In 2005 it launched Yahoo! Music, which provides Internet radio, music videos, news, and original programming, and which became in 2007 the #1 online music site for audience reach and total time spent. The company also purchased the photo-sharing Web services business Flickr, which in 2007 had a repository of nearly one billion images. Other acquisitions include an online social event calendar company and the social bookmark site del.icio.us.

Yahoo! is now one of the most trafficked Internet destinations, providing a huge array of services in four major categories: content, search and marketplace, community, and personalization. Led by CEO and "Chief Yahoo" Jerry Yang, key technologist and "Chief Yahoo" David Filo, and President Susan Decker, Sunnyvale-based Yahoo! is the world's largest network of integrated services, with more than 500 million users and offices around the globe. As it looks to the future and offering increasing numbers of tools and solutions, the company remains committed to connecting people to their passions and to providing the power to create, gather, and share information.

ust about anything can be sold on eBay.com, the eBay Inc.-managed Internet auction and shopping Website established in 1995 by Pierre Omidyar. In fact, the first item sold on eBay was a broken laser pointer. When Omidyar contacted the winning bidder to make sure he understood that the item he had bought was broken, the man e-mailed back yes—that he collected broken laser pointers.

When Omidyar launched eBay.com, then known as AuctionWeb, he was trying to determine how providing equal access to information and opportunities would affect the efficiency of the marketplace. Judging by the satisfaction of the millions of people and businesses that buy and sell goods and services on eBay every day, Omidyar and his company, now based in San Jose and led by CEO and president Meg Whitman, have shown that a level playing field does indeed benefit Internet commerce.

Everything from art to cell phones to coins to collectibles, consumer electronics, dolls and bears, garden equipment, musical instruments, real estate, travel services, and so much more can be listed for sale on eBay. com. Sales take place through either open-bidding auctions or fixed-price "storefronts," and the company provides sellers with tips on how to make the best sale possible.

eBay Inc. also provides sites and services with which users can make payments, communicate with voice and video, shop, rent housing, and post classified ads. In 2002, eBay acquired PayPal, an Internet service that enables individuals and businesses to securely and easily send and receive payments online. Using the most advanced proprietary fraud-prevention systems, PayPal's millions of registered account holders worldwide pay bills and receive funds on and off the eBay site.

In 2005, eBay Inc. also acquired Shopping.com, the pioneering shopping site that offers consumers millions of products from thousand of merchants around the world. eBay Inc. also purchased Rent.com in 2005. This site—the most visited online apartment-listing service in the United States—features more than 20,000 properties across the U.S. and provides extensive apartment-related information, including availability, rental rates, and roommate search resources.

To help people share ideas and come together at the local level, eBay Inc. also offers numerous online classifieds Websites in hundred of cities and regions. These sites include Gumtree.com, LoQUo.com, and mobile.de. eBay also has a minority investment in classifieds pioneer craigslist.com.

By providing so many online services and powerful Internet platforms of choice, eBay enables people around the world to explore opportunities and innovate together. The company's newest features—eBay Express, on which select eBay.com items are mirrored and customers can use a shopping cart to buy from multiple sellers; eBay Blogs and eBay Community Wiki, which provide discussion boards and reviews and guides; and eBay Mobile, which offers text messaging and other mobile services—promise to keep eBay's passionate community of users communicating and trading for years to come.

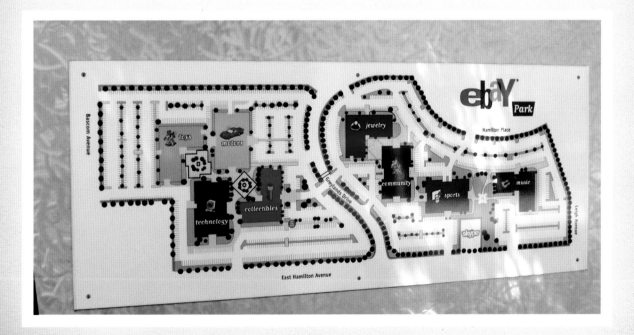

Chapter 19: The Sky's the Limit

If 1995's incandescent IPO by Netscape shone a light on the opportunities of the Internet, the closing years of the 20th Century saw Silicon Valley in the global glare of world attention. Anything was possible, expectations were boundless and people were ready for a rocket ride to the heights.

Helping fuel this was the U.S. Supreme Court's rejection of the Communications Decency Act, a much-disputed provision of the Telecommunications Act of 1996. Until that ruling, no one knew if the Internet would be an unfiltered, limitless universe or a government-regulated entity like radio and television. But now, the limits were off and the Net could grow. Anyone could access the network and anyone could decide what went online. The Web became a powerful, liberating force that brought people together and shaped new businesses.

Yahoo! Corporate Headquarters

Take Yahoo!, for instance. Founded by Stanford University graduate students Jerry Yang and David Filo in 1995 as a quirky list of favorite links, it became the go-to site of the 90s. A billion Web pages were coming into bloom, and Yahoo! was a favorite way to find them. When Yahoo! went public in 1996, Yang and Filo became instant millionaires.

People also wanted to find other people and to communicate with them. Hotmail, one of the first Web services to give away e-mail for free, went from zero users in 1995 to 30 million subscribers only 30 months later. At the end of 10 years, it would have 215 million users.

And then there was expanding commerce, basic buying and selling. Online bookseller and burgeoning retailing giant Amazon.com, which had been founded within months of the launch of Yahoo!, had proven that people were becoming ready to eschew bricks-and-mortar stores in favor of shopping from home via computers.

amazon.com®

Would people also want to sell things to other people through the medium of an online auction? Pierre Omidyar had hoped so when, as a part-time experiment, he launched Auction Web in 1995. Transactions at the site grew so far beyond expectations by 1996 that Omidyar left his full-time job at software maker General Magic and, working with Jeff Skoll, morphed Auction Web into eBay in 1997. When it went public in 1998, stock purchasers made it an instant success and gave eBay the fifth-highest first-day gain in the market's history. Omidyar, Skoll and new CEO Meg Whitman, who had been brought in from Hasbro, joined the ranks of instant millionaires. At the company's San Jose headquarters, employees abandoned their cubicles in a delirious conga line.

1996

Israel elects conservative Likud Party leader Benjamin Netanyahu as its prime minister.

TWA Flight 800, a Boeing 747 with 212 passengers and 18 crew members aboard, crashes into the Atlantic Ocean off Long Island, NY. There are no survivors.

Russia re-elects populist Boris Yeltsin as president.

Terrorists bomb a U.S. military base in Dhahran, Saudi Arabia, causing 514 casualties.

The XXVI Olympic Games in Atlanta are marred by a terrorist bomb killing one person.

*E*Trade Financial San Francisco Office*

Whitman's former boss, who had asked her why she was leaving the East for the other coast, called her to say, "Now I get it." The legend — and the lure — of IPOs making millionaires of Silicon Valley risk-takers was in full swing.

In the first quarter of 1997 alone, 147 new companies came into being. "It's an elixir that you breathe in the air as you come into this part of the world," Christos M. Cotasakos, CEO of Palo Alto-based online brokerage E*Trade was quoted. His company had gone public itself in 1996, raising $46 million. "I have never seen anything like this. This is Mecca."

BusinessWeek noted in 1997 that five Valley powerhouses — Intel, Cisco Systems, 3Com, Sun Microsystems and Netscape -– boasted a higher market value than General Motors, Ford and Chrysler combined.

So many people were getting in on what was becoming a Silicon Valley gold rush that few noticed in 1998 when Stanford University Ph.D students Sergey Brin and Larry Page started yet another Internet search engine they dubbed Google. But they'd notice later.

Even a company that had been struggling, Apple Computer, underwent a resurrection in this vibrant climate, although in Apple's case it took the return of Steve Jobs. The charismatic co-founder, who had been pushed out more than a decade earlier, returned to Apple as a consultant in 1996 and took over as CEO in 1997. To stop the company's slide against Microsoft, Jobs cut back or eliminated some departments and research programs, stopped licensing Mac clones, initiated an on-line store and reduced the product line to a handful of desktop and laptop computers. As a result, the company announced in 1997 that they had turned a profit for the first time in three years, and observers felt it had survived — smaller, but wiser. They were proven right in 1998 when Apple introduced the iMac, a high-design, consumer-oriented personal computer that racked up 150,000 orders before it went on sale in retail stores and gave the company another yearly profit.

1997

New class of drugs and combination therapy offer more hope of longevity to AIDS sufferers.

Theodore John Kaczynski, the Unabomber who targeted technological and industrial companies with mail bombs, was arrested outside his cabin near Lincoln, Montana.

Britain's Princess Diana dies in a violent car crash in Paris.

The successful cloning of a sheep named Dolly touches off scientific and ethical debate.

China takes control of Hong Kong, ending status as a British Crown Colony.

Legal troubles caught up with industry giant Microsoft in 1998, when U.S. Attorney General Janet Reno and attorney generals from 20 states and the District of Columbia sued the Redmond, Washington, company for violating anti-trust laws. CEO Bill Gates denied his company had done anything wrong, and Microsoft introduced a new operating system, Windows 98.

When America Online swallowed Netscape for $4 billion, attorneys charged that Microsoft's practices had crushed the latter company and said the deal should be voided. That didn't happen, the deal went through, and AOL's status as a Web portal increased.

As the 1900s drew to a close, technology was everyone's darling. As *Time* magazine technology correspondent Chris Taylor acknowledged, " . . . 1999 was a year of unassailable confidence. With the Internet gold rush in full flow, thousands of us have been seduced by the promise of paper riches at the end of the online rainbow."

At the Super Bowl in January, there were commercials for dot-com companies competing for viewers' attention with those for more traditional products such as beer and automobiles. Revenues in e-commerce — itself a relatively new term — were expected to triple during the holiday season. By millennium's end, more than 200 million people were going online for information, business, communications and fun.

Online word-of-mouth made a movie, "*The Blair Witch Project*," a hit. The terms "day trader" and MP3 became common, the latter the result of Napster, a once obscure file-sharing program, that became a global network for trading digital music for free. The music industry responded with multiple lawsuits charging copyright infringement, and the resulting court actions reduced Napster to a mere shadow of its former self. But the genie was out of the bottle, and the traditional music industry would never again be the same.

In Microsoft's ongoing legal battle, Federal Judge Thomas Penfield Jackson issued findings of fact that the company had indeed engaged in monopolistic practices. The U.S. Justice Department had made its charges stick, but the software giant was avoiding being broken up and trading breakup for shakeup. Bill Gates, who had barely recognized the Internet four years earlier, led the charge as Microsoft announced its intention to focus exclusively on Web services.

President Bill Clinton became the first U.S. president to take part in an online chat. His experience with the Web had been less pleasant in 1998 when online gadfly Matt Drudge broke the story of the president's Oval Office

1997
Labour candidate Tony Blair wins election as Britain's prime minister.

Timothy McVeigh is found guilty of bombing the federal building in Oklahoma City.

1998
Historic agreement was made which brought final peace to Northern Ireland.

"Ethnic cleansing" leads to crisis in Kosovo.

Terrorists bomb U.S. embassies in Nairobi, Kenya, and Dar Es Salaam, Tanzania.

U.S. and Britain launch air strikes against Iraq, aimed at destroying their weaponry.

- 156 -

Rambus's opening day on the NASDAQ.

dalliances and touched off a political firestorm. The Web was where more people were turning to get their news fast. The term "blog," shorthand for Web log, joined our lexicon.

Video game sales, boosted by the popularity of online gaming, began to top sales of movie tickets for the first time. People were beginning to surf the Net on their cell phones, their pagers, and even some of their game consoles.

Stocks in Silicon Valley firms continued to climb, particularly those of networking equipment companies: Foundry was up 632 percent, Sycamore up 528 percent, Juniper up 702 percent. The Dow Jones Industrial Average got a makeover, with such old-line companies as Union Carbide, Sears, Chevron and Goodyear making way for newcomers including Intel and Microsoft. The latter were the first two companies from the tech-heavy NASDAQ exchange to be invited to join the index of indexes. The NASDAQ itself was breaking records of its own, with the one-time junior exchange topping 3,000, led by Sun Microsystems and Apple. Investors were saying, "Tech stocks rule, industrials drool."

There were fears, though, that a Y2K bug might spoil the debut of the new century. The crisis had its origins in the early days of computing, when programmers writing code for computers decided to save space by including only two digits for the year. Thus, when 1999 gave way to 2000, people worried that many computers would read 1900 instead, causing everything from confusion to computer crashes and mammoth loss of data. But what programmers had done, programmers could undo. New code was written, patches were distributed online, and as the new year approached, most of the worries had eased.

A new year, a new millennium, a new economy, a new optimism.

What could possibly go wrong?

1999

NATO goes to war over human rights in Kosovo.

A massacre of students at Columbine High School in Littleton, Colo., stuns the nation.

A U.S. district judge finds Microsoft guilty of being a monopoly.

A vote in the U.S. Senate fails to impeach President Bill Clinton.

John F. Kennedy Jr., his wife and sister-in-law die in the crash of a small plane off Mass.

Fears spread over the perceived threat to computers of the Y2K or Millennium Bug.

- 157 -

In today's competitive business environment, in which the costs of succeeding and the pressure to improve the bottom line continually increase, companies must find ways to reap the most value from every dollar spent on services, direct materials, and indirect goods to improve their profits, mitigate risk, and gain competitive advantage.

"Spend management" is the fastest, most efficient way to address this critical challenge. Ariba, Inc., headquartered in Sunnyvale, Calif., invented the concept and is the leading global provider of solutions that drive spend management.

Ariba was founded by seven executives who wanted to automate the purchase of common supplies and services. In 1996 they incorporated as Ariba, Inc., and soon had a prototype product. Licensing deals with major corporations, including Cisco Systems, Advanced Micro Devices, and Octel, quickly followed. Ariba's first product, now known as Ariba Buyer, was shipped in 1997.

Much of 1998 was devoted to recruiting expert personnel and to improving Ariba Buyer. Then, in 1999, the company entered the business-to-business marketplace with a supplier network. After going public that year, Ariba established strategic alliances to provide e-payment services, logistics commerce services, and software for creating communities of online buyers and sellers. In 2000 the company shipped two new products—Ariba Dynamic Trade and Ariba Marketplace—and acquired SupplierMarket.com, which led to the launch of Ariba Sourcing. With these capabilities, and the company's July 1, 2004, merger with FreeMarkets, Inc., which brought commodity and category specialists to the table, Ariba revolutionized the way global business is done.

With Robert Calderoni at the helm, Ariba delivers superior spend management results to more than 550 customers around the globe. Ariba's solutions are used to source more than $450 million in goods and services each day, process a purchase order every two seconds, manage purchase transaction volumes twice the size of eBay, and manage more than $170 billion in procurement annually. Combining speed, sustainability, coverage, and flexibility, Ariba drives exceptional enterprise-wide savings and operational efficiency via seven spend management solutions:

Robert Calderoni,
Chairman and Chief Executive Officer

- **Ariba Spend Visibility**, which enables decisionmakers to identify, quantify, and prioritize all opportunities throughout the purchasing life cycle

- **Ariba Sourcing**, which enables companies to use the most appropriate strategies for sourcing all categories of spend

- **Ariba Contract Management**, which lets companies unlock the value of their contracts portfolios through business process improvement and automation

- **Ariba Procurement and Expense Management**, which enables companies to leverage their organization for better spend compliance

- **Ariba Invoice and Payment**, which automates paper-intensive activities for accurate, streamlined electronic invoicing and payment

- **Ariba Supplier Management**, which supports supplier discovery, evaluation, and relationship management

- **Ariba Supplier Network**, the world's largest open trading network, through which buyers and suppliers collaborate and transact business in real time

These spend management solutions provide much more than enterprise resource planning, or ERP. While ERP is about procuring, spend management provides a proactive strategy for taking advantage of opportunities for significant savings and greatly increased efficiencies.

Ariba's solutions, as well as its deployment models—Software as a Service, on-premise, hosted, and outsourced—allow customers to adopt the right solution to meet their unique needs. Ariba's unmatched domain expertise enables businesses of all sizes to achieve operational excellence in today's dynamic global environment.

From Left to Right: Jim Frankola - Chief Finanacial Officer, Kevin Costello - Chief Commercial Officer, H. Tayloe Stansbury - Executive Vice President, Products & Operations, Kent Parker - Executive Vice President and General Manager, Ariba Global Services Organization

Covad is transforming communications through broadband innovation. The company was founded following the adoption of the Telecommunications Act of 1996, which made it possible for companies like Covad to provide new telecommunications options. Covad quickly became the first to commercially deploy DSL in the U.S. and now, through continuous innovation, offers a broad portfolio of cutting-edge data, voice, and wireless solutions. With its acquisition of other Silicon Valley success stories GoBeam and NextWeb to provide VoIP and broadband wireless, respectively, Covad is the only nationwide facilities-based next-generation telecommunications provider.

Covad's Network Operations Center in San Jose, California

Headquartered in San Jose, California, with approximately 1,000 employees, Covad focuses on sales to small and medium-sized businesses and is a leading provider of next-generation broadband services to those companies. Covad also is a leader in providing communication services to homes, through strategic partners such as AT&T and EarthLink, and operates the nation's largest ADSL2+ (asymmetric DSL) network, servicing more than 14 million homes with data speeds up to 25 mbps.

From its beginnings in California, Covad now offers high-bandwidth service in 44 states and 235 metropolitan areas and saw its growth services such as business class broadband, voice, and wireless, grow by 30% over the last year. The company's growth reflects its employees' talent and energy and its commitment to innovation and helping customers get more from their broadband connection and has earned it numerous industry awards.

President and CEO Charles E. Hoffman sees no end to Covad's innovation and expansion: "As we celebrate Covad's first decade of achievements, we look forward to continued success, increased growth, and ongoing inspiration from the dynamic environment of Silicon Valley."

Covad Wireless Tower

Covad's President and CEO, Charles E. Hoffman

"We started making pictures that were so photo realistic that we couldn't believe that we had done it in a way with non-impact printing, which was what the whole field was called, ink jet being only one part of it. And I guess the most exciting part of the project, once we made the pictures, we started making many pictures, and reproduction quality was beyond our imagination. I knew we had done something. We weren't sure of the impact."

— *Annette Jaffe*
Developer of ink jet technology

"One of the advances was the ear implant which is a spin-off from the micromachining group at Stanford. This is a thin plastic needle that has a bunch of electrodes on it and you insert it in the ear in a deaf person and you can excite the nerves in the ear electrically through this little array of probes and you can actually restore hearing. They do this in some children now, you can restore hearing in totally deaf children and it's just a fantastic advance."

— *Kurt Petersen*
Father of micromachining

"I recently heard a lecture which was recounting the history of the main disease that our laser treated, which was the condition known as diabetic retinopathy, and the statistics are that in 1966, if you contracted diabetic retinopathy, there was a 50 percent chance that you would be blind within 10 years. Today that chance has been reduced to one percent. So we're very proud of the contribution."

— *James Hobart*
Founder, Coherent, Inc.

"Engineers are all identified with their own product. And they all have a desire to get their product out and they want it to be the best product of that type in the world. And there's a lot of other engineers looking over their shoulder or they ask questions within the group because any idea that's a good idea that they can incorporate into their product makes it a better product and they're happy to do it because the identity of it is still with them."

— *Robert C. Dobkin*
Analog Engineer
Founder, Linear Technology

"The prostate in males at about 55 is growing and getting bigger and this prevents the flow of liquids and often needs to be operated on. It's called prostate hyperplasia. It's done through a uteroscope that is introduced and you try to remove the piece of the prostate that is blocking the channel. We use a procedure that uses a laser with a color of light that you can not see, but that cuts and cauterizes the prostate cuts. Meaning there is no bleeding. We have been able to make this procedure now an outpatient procedure with very little cauterized time and little discomfort for the patient."

— *Bernard Couillaud*
Former CEO, Coherent

"The most complex things we used to build were buildings and cities that are intricate and have patterns all over the place. Nowadays it's no longer a city that's the most complicated thing that we, as mankind, fabricate. It's silicon chips. These chips hold an enormous amount of complexity that we can hardly ever hold in our own minds and they also invite the creation of software to drive them."

— *Isaac Chuang*
Inventor

he year 1996 was a singular year not only for Silicon Valley but for technology users the world over. It was during that year that Sunnyvale, Calif.–based Palm, Inc., then known as Palm Computing, ignited a mobile- computing revolution by introducing its groundbreaking Palm® Pilot handheld electronic organizer.

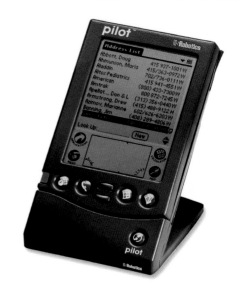

Palm sold 1 million Pilot organizers in the product's first 18 months – an adoption rate faster than the IBM PC, Macintosh and even the microwave oven.

The Palm Pilot allowed users to store phone numbers, addresses, to-do lists, and other essential information for navigating daily life and to take it with them wherever they went. Due primarily to two breakthrough features—the ability to synchronize easily with a computer and unprecedented ease of use—the handheld was an instant success and sensation, and quickly became the fastest-selling consumer technology product of all time.

Founded in 1992 by acclaimed inventor Jeff Hawkins, who now holds nine patents for a variety of handheld devices and features, Palm Computing was established to give people access to their most important electronic information without the need to be seated in front of their desktop computer. Since that time, the company has remained focused on this founding vision and delivered category-defining, software-rich mobile solutions that enable people to work, play, and communicate with family, friends, and colleagues around the world. Today, Palm products help keep users connected to their work and home, letting them send and receive e-mail, browse the Web on the go, and keep their favorite files, music, photos, and videos with them.

The Palm® V handheld computer -- with sleek style as well as productivity capabilities -- was the first Palm product to charm gadget fans and trendsetters, marking a tipping point for mainstream market adoption.

The device that started it all, the Palm Pilot 1000, has been followed by ever-more smart and powerful models. In February 1999, the company launched the Palm V handheld, whose sleek design and smaller size turned the mobile computer into a personal statement. That Palm handheld was quickly followed by the revolutionary Palm VII, the first wireless solution that delivered access to the Web. Soon after, in 2002, Palm debuted its Zire™ line of handhelds; the Palm Z22, with its $99 price tag, made mobile computing not only freeing and fun but affordable as well.

Palm products have touched people's lives, appearing in Broadway shows, major Hollywood movies, reality TV, New Yorker cartoons, and on the red carpet.

Treo smartphones, available on carrier networks around the world, combine a phone with email, web browsing, messaging, multimedia, calendar, contacts and more.

The year 2002 also saw the introduction of Palm's Tungsten™ line of innovative handhelds, which gave business customers the power and mobility they need to work any time, anywhere. Today the Tungsten E2 provides upscale, premium features at a budget-conscious price and the Palm TX handheld makes Wi-Fi and Bluetooth® wireless capabilities affordable.

The Palm Treo™ 600 smartphone, introduced in 2003, was another revolutionary product, setting the standard for smartphones that integrate phone and computer seamlessly. In 2006, the Treo 700w led the field again, bringing the Palm's hallmark ease of use to Windows Mobile® customers.

Over the past decade, Palm products have collected data in space, survived a Mt. Everest climb, closed million-dollar deals, and won the hearts of customers around the globe. As the next era of mobile computing dawns, the company looks forward to an exciting future, committed to building the most compelling and intuitive mobile-computing solutions in the world.

palm Palm Headquarters
Sunnyvale, California

oogle co-founder Larry Page has said that, "The perfect search engine would understand exactly what you mean and give back exactly what you want." Since Page and co-founder Sergey Brin collaborated on their first search engine, which they called BackRub, for the way it could analyze "back links" pointing to different Websites, they have been focused on developing just such an engine, and along the way have redefined the way people worldwide view and use the Internet.

Page and Brin met in 1995 at Stanford University. Interested in solving one of computing's biggest challenges—retrieving pertinent information from huge stores of data—they collaborated on a search technology, building computer housings in Page's dorm room and scouring their department's loading docks for newly arrived computers they could borrow for their network. In 1998, with their new approach to search technology perfected, they began to call on prospective licensors—the two were not interested in building their own company.

But when Yahoo! founder and friend David Filo encouraged Page and Brin to start their own search engine company—and when none of the day's major portal companies jumped on their technology—the two made the decision to create a start-up. With $100,000 from Sun Microsystems co-founder Andy Bechtolsheim, who took one look at their demo and wrote out a check, and another $900,000 from family, friends, and acquaintances, Page and Brin joined with newly hired director of technology Craig Silverstein and established their corporation in a garage in Menlo Park.

At that time, Google.com, still in beta form, was fulfilling 10,000 search queries a day. Now Google—a play on the word "googol," which refers to the number represented by 1 followed by 100 zeroes, reflecting the company's mission to organize the seemingly infinite amount of information on the Web—receives several hundred million queries each day through its various services, which include searching, shopping on, and browsing the Web; e-mailing and chatting; creating, organizing, and sharing information; connecting with customers; locating places; and getting information on the go.

Like every other year in which Google has been in business, 2007 was filled with innovation and growth. The year began with a partnership with China Mobile, the world's largest mobile telecommunications provider as well as a collaboration with Samsung that placed Google products and services on selected Samsung phones. The company also updated Google maps for mobile use and enabled users to customize maps, added new features to Google Groups that changed it from a message board forum to an easy-to-build "home on the Web" in which people share information, began working with SalesForce.com to give companies better tools for building their business online, and announced its first steps toward universal searching, in which one search results in integrated video, news, books, images, and local information, among many others advances.

With so much innovation already under its belt, what will be next for this global, green company that employs more than 10,000 people but retains a small-company feel, with clustered work spaces, couches for people and pets, roller hockey games in the parking lot, and lunches and dinners provided for staff? Google invites you to give them your opinion by checking out their not-quite-ready-for-prime-time ideas at the company's "technology playground," labs.google.com.

n 2007, manufacturing and services giant Tyco Electronics became an independent, publicly traded company, but the powerhouse companies on which it's based—Raychem Corporation and AMP Incorporated—were founded more than 50 years ago. In 1999, both companies became part of Tyco Electronics, which has continued to build on their heritage of engineering and innovation. Tyco Electronics is now is the largest supplier of passive electronic components in the world, and the global leader in connectors and interconnection devices.

Maintaining a major presence in Menlo Park and Redwood City, California, Tyco Electronics produces products that enable cost-effective solutions across a variety of industries. These include heat shrink tubing, which finds use in the power utility and telecommunications markets; point-of-sale touchscreens that quickly let servers transmit food orders to their kitchens; surge arresters that help protect electrical power distribution lines; and re-settable fuses that protect cellular phones from short circuits. Tyco Electronics also offers products used in advanced automotive systems to enhance consumers' driving experiences.

Through accountability, teamwork, and innovation, and by leveraging the legacy of Raychem expertise and experience across its many businesses, Tyco Electronics provides its customers with leading-edge passive electronic, wireless, and fiber-optic components. By remaining committed to bringing a performance advantage to every technology, product, and service it provides, Tyco Electronics is ready to continue growing with—and helping to shape—technology in the 21st century.

Elo Touchscreen

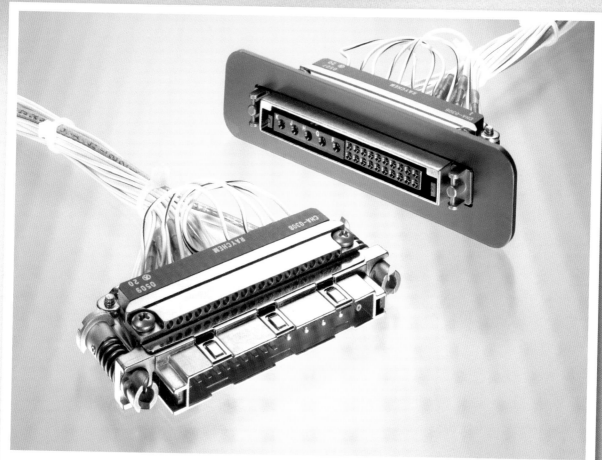

High performance connectors

Heat shrink tubing products

The success story began more than a quarter-century ago, when current president and CEO T. J. Rodgers founded the company in a small rented space near the Great America amusement park in Santa Clara, California. Each succeeding chapter—from a flurry of new generations of programmable products to a robust diversification effort—has chronicled a fiercely competitive and dynamic Silicon Valley mainstay. In 2006, Cypress broke

Cypress is a recognized leader in the solar power industry. In 2002, the company acquired SunPower Corp., maker of the industry's most efficient silicon solar cells. SunPower, listed independently on the Nasdaq stock exchange, has since become Cypress's largest business unit. This photo shows solar panels on the rooftops of two buildings at Cypress's headquarters in San Jose, Calif.

T.J. Rodgers is the founder, president and CEO of Cypress Semiconductor Corp. An accomplished inventor in his own right, with 15 patents to his credit, Rodgers is widely recognized as a proponent of free-market capitalism and Silicon Valley innovation and independence. He has helped to spearhead the fresh wave of thinking in the Valley about solar power and other forms of alternative energy.

the $1 billion revenue mark for the second time in its history. And, in the second quarter of 2007, the company set a new quarterly revenue record.

From the get-go, the outspoken Rodgers set the bar high. In the company's first business plan, he said that Cypress would deliver products superior to the competition in every measure of performance. Building on a groundbreaking SRAM (static random access memory) product line—described by many as the Maserati of memory technology—Cypress quickly introduced programmable memories and programmable logic devices, enabling design engineers to rapidly customize a chip's functionality. The high performance and flexibility of those early products landed the fast-growing company on the covers of national business publications, such as *The Wall Street Journal*, *Forbes*, *Fortune*, and *BusinessWeek*. Indeed, the groundwork had been laid for generations of future programmable products and solutions.

Making good on Rodgers's early proclamation, Cypress's products have continued to outperform the competition.

In the 1990s, Cypress helped pioneer the emerging Universal Serial Bus (USB) standard. Cypress's USB solutions remain extremely successful today, with one recent solution enabling next-generation, multimedia cell phones to download music and data from a PC up to 10 times faster than competitive solutions do. Cypress also developed its first programmable clock generator during the 1990s.

Then came the dot.com crash of 2001. While other companies struggled to formulate a new strategy, Rodgers quickly mobilized his troops in a new effort: diversification. The strategy bore fruit with the innovative Programmable System-on-Chip™, or PSoC®, mixed-signal array. Combining powerful, programmable analog and digital blocks with on-board memory and computing resources, PSoC today is a key ingredient in thousands of leading-edge products, including cellular phones, portable media players, digital still cameras, personal computers, automobiles, fitness equipment, remote controls, consumer appliances, and high-definition TVs.

Diversification moved to the next level in 2002, when Cypress acquired SunPower Corporation, a start-up that produces the industry's most efficient silicon solar cells. SunPower's solar cells and modules—which generate as much as 50% more power per unit area than conventional solar technologies—have a

Cypress's mission is to become a leading provider of programmable solutions in systems everywhere. PSoC®, Cypress's Programmable System on Chip™ (pictured above), is the flagship product of this strategy. The PSoC device targets a $13 billion market, providing room for robust growth.

uniquely attractive, all-black appearance and are ideal for both commercial and residential installations. SunPower, which leverages Cypress's manufacturing and management expertise, completed its initial public offering on the NASDAQ stock exchange in 2005, leading to industry-wide acclaim for Cypress's decision to strike out in a bold direction.

Capacitive-touch-sensing buttons on the side of the adidas_1 DLX Runner shoe, powered by Cypress's PSoC® programmable mixed-signal array, enable the shoe's cushioning to be adjusted to the runner's comfort level.

The year 2006 brought more changes, as Cypress discontinued expensive process R&D aimed at shrinking chip size in pursuit of "Moore's Law" and expanded production outsourcing to limit capital expenditures. Both moves substantially improved the company's financial performance. From 2005 to 2006, Cypress's share price increased 43.8%, far outpacing the single-digit increases of the SOXX and S&P semiconductor indices.

Cypress's management team rang the opening bell at the New York Stock Exchange in May 2006, celebrating 20 years as a public company. In 2007, Cypress posted record revenue of $1.09 billion. Its growth in recent years has been driven largely by its PSoC and SunPower business units.

In October of 2006, Cypress framed a new mission statement that now hangs in every company building worldwide: "We will transform Cypress from a traditional broad-line semiconductor company to the leading supplier of programmable solutions in systems everywhere." Cypress's global customer companies, including Cisco, Hitachi, Logitech, LG, Adidas, Lenovo, HP, Pentax, and Nintendo, can attest to the company's staying power and to continued progress in its programmable solutions strategy.

A Look into the Future

"We tend to think that what we have done historically that has yielded a degree of success would continue to be the way that you do it in the future. And quite often, failure is the only mechanism that shows you that you must change."

— *Finis Conner*
Founder, Conner Peripherals

"We picked up a lot of ideas about the importance of culture and how different groups are successful doing things in different ways, but in ways that we could incorporate portions here at Applied. I think that focus has enabled us to develop a rather unique global community, and I think that type of company is clearly what's required in the future-in the next century. And I think also that it is important for students and others to understand that that's the way the world is probably going to be in the 21st century."

— *Jim Morgan*
Chairman of the Board,
Applied Materials

"The generation that's coming behind us is going to enjoy technology. They're going to know what they want. It's going to be really clear what hits and what doesn't hit. There's not going to be a lot of ambiguity about it. Technology will not be the thing that sells them. They couldn't care less if it doesn't solve some problem in their life or enhance something. And I think when they see it, there are going to be big markets for it."

— *Chris Malachowsky*
Founder, NVIDIA

"I look at Silicon Valley as still the seed growth area for the computing industry and the future of information technology in the world."

— *John Warnock*
Founder, Adobe Systems

A Look into the Future

"The demands are going to be vast, and the solutions are to create what I call the *technology cascade*: a number of different technologies assembled in tandem with a corporate management team that understands the whole concept of the total development cycle — how to bring this technology to create the superior products of the future."

— *Alejandro Zaffaroni*
Founder, Syntex, Alza, and Affymax

"What is happening in the Valley is that you have a sense of the best and the brightest technical minds in the world. They congregate here. They come here from all over Europe, from all over the Far East, from all over India and the Americas. They find people like themselves, they find an environment which is very receptive to the energy and vitality they bring. The art form today is no longer painting and sculpture, but it is creating patterns that you etch in silicon or you etch and print into the circuit board — the breadth of knowledge that is required to do what we do, the new vitality that is brought to bear, the sense of the future and the belief in the future which was also part of the Renaissance."

— *Frederico Faggin*
Developer of the Microprocessor
Founder, Zilog, Inc.

"The use of massively parallel computers and databases and gene mapping is going to be extraordinarily important as we move forward. And you really will see a confluence of biotechnology, engineering, and information sciences, where one is enabling the other-specifically information science is enabling advances in bioengineering."

— *Larry Ellison*
Founder, Oracle

A Look into the Future

"A lot of people don't appreciate how much technology was in the original Apple design. The world's first single-board computer, the whole computer on one board. It was the first computer in the word that had RAM on the main circuit board. It was the first computer that had a programming language built in RAM. It was the first computer that interacted seamlessly with a television set. It was the world's first computer that had color graphics, or any graphics, for that matter. And so when I saw that, I said, you know, this really has possibilities, and I really want these guys to succeed because I'd like to buy one of these some day." — Reminiscing about his first meeting with Jobs and Wozniak.

— **Mike Markkula**
Founder & Chairman of the Board, Apple Computer

"What I see for the future is that instead of a laptop, you'll have a very small computer that won't have a display or keyboard. It's just something that you'll carry in your hip pocket, or your coat pocket, or your handbag. If you're traveling, you might keep it in your luggage. You wouldn't access it by things connected to it like cables; you'd access it wirelessly. You might have an earphone in your ear and a microphone somehow positioned, all of which would have a radio that would talk to the computer. I think we'll see extremely powerful machines in an amazingly small space and it will make a very big difference to how we use computers in the future."

— **Vaughn Pratt**
Founder, Sun Microsystems

"I'm optimistic about the future. It may not seem in 1993 that we are eliminating war from the world-but, in fact we are in the process of eliminating war from the world. We now have succeeded in controlling the threat of destruction of the world, of the human race possibly, in a great nuclear war."

— **Linus Pauling**
Nobel Laureate: Peace & Chemistry

Chapter 20: The Bubble Bursts

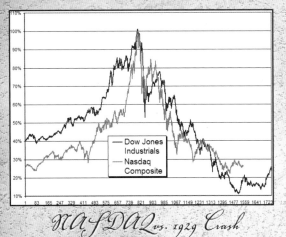

NASDAQ vs. 1929 Crash

The millennium dawned brightly. The effects of the Y2K bug were slight to none. Optimism about the future still seemed high. But there had been a few dark clouds earlier, and by the end of 2000 they were developing into a full-fledged storm.

During the previous five years, there had been occasional warnings from analysts that what went up inevitably had to come down. These were swept aside by rising expectations, by stock market prices that continued to climb, by the rush of companies getting venture capital funding if their names ended in "dot-com." There had been warnings that new companies without solid business practices or solid profits had to fail. These also were swept aside as "old economy." The "new economy," some said, now held sway and if some dot-com companies weren't yet profitable, the ever-surging growth of the Internet soon would make them so.

But not even a gold rush mentality could repeal the laws of gravity or basic economics. As 2000 progressed, investors fearful about a lack of short-term profits began getting nervous and backing out. As more and more fled, a stock market roller coaster began, with the most common direction being down.

As CNET.com summed up at year's end, "It was a tough year for technology. Investors fled the online shopping sector . . . leaving Web companies to go belly-up and giving traditional retailers a leg up. After starting 2000 with strong sales, computer makers were blindsided by soft demand in the second quarter and the collapse of growth during the Christmas holidays. The 451 IPOs in 2000 (posted) an average loss of 15 percent by mid-December, compared with an average gain of 194 percent in 1999. Venture capitalists are still flush with cash, but they have become highly skeptical of most business plans and don't think many start-ups are worthy of their money."

Explanations were sought. CNN.com ascribed the dot-com implosion to "a combination of poor business planning, intense competition and weak advertising markets (that) pushed scores of dot-com companies to the brink, wiping out billions of dollars in market capitalization and sending share prices tumbling."

Most emblematic of the collapse was Pets.com, launched as an online business selling pet supplies and accessories direct to customers. Its striking commercial featuring a sock-puppet dog captivated Super Bowl television viewers in January. The company went public in February, but never managed to attain the critical mass of customers sufficient to support an ambitious business plan. By November, with venture capitalists declining further funding, Pets.com closed its doors. Its stock, which had sold for $11 per share in February, was worth 19 cents at the time of liquidation.

Pets.com Closure Article

2000
After a 36-day battle over vote counts and "hanging chads," George W. Bush is president.

Researchers complete a draft of the human genome, the blueprint for the human body.

The Russian submarine Kursk sinks in the Barents Sea, with no survivors.

Companies are pushed to the brink by the implosion of the dot-com bubble.

2001
Radical Muslims directed by Osama bin Laden fly hijacked airliners into the World

Trade Center and the Pentagon.

- 176 -

WebVan Trucks in San Francisco

A similar fate would await Webvan, a Foster City-based online credit-and-delivery grocery business. It, too, had ambitious aspirations, but a lack of management experience in the supermarket industry hampered those efforts, as did lavish spending, which far exceeded sales growth. Webvan reportedly contracted for $1 billion worth of warehouses, bought 30 powerful Sun Microsystems servers, dozens of Compaq computers and several Cisco Systems routers, more than eighty 21-inch color monitors and more than 100 Herman Miller chairs topping $800 each. The company ran out of money in 2001 and donated its stores of non-perishable foodstuffs to local food banks.

Webvan's collapse wasn't the only bad news of 2001. Even before the terrorist attacks of Sept. 11 weakened an already shaky economy, most of the high-tech industry was caught in a slump of unprecedented severity. Revenues for the 2,400 member companies of Semiconductor Equipment and Materials International saw revenues plunge more than 30 percent from the previous year. Dataquest said the chip sector had suffered "the worst industry decline in the history of the market." Even market leader Intel saw a revenue drop of more than 22 percent, and it was estimated that the semiconductor industry worldwide had lost $100 billion. Personal computer sales fell for only the second time ever. Palm reported a 44 percent decline after celebrating four consecutive quarters of 100 percent revenue growth a year earlier. Cisco Systems posted its first quarterly loss in 11 years as a public company. Sun Microsystems had a yearly revenue plunge of 43 percent. Exodus Communications was forced into Chapter 11 bankruptcy protection.

Carnage from the dot-com meltdown was everywhere. *News.com* summed up the ensuing blame game by ascribing the collapse to "day traders who gambled on obscure companies, mid-level engineers who cashed in stock options and retired at 29, Wall Street analysts who preached 'eyeballs, stickiness and price-to-sales ratios,' forecasting companies that predicted exponential growth and business publications that canonized the rich and gave others hope of striking similar fortunes."

Even through the gloom, though, there were some possibly positive notes.

Apple Computer had taken a big loss in January 2001, but quickly adjusted and got back in the black for the rest of the year, aided by the introduction in October of a new product, the iPod. The tiny personal digital music player, a Mac-compatible device with a 5 GB hard drive, was said by Steve Jobs to put "1,000 songs in your pocket."

The widespread industry contraction pushed Hewlett-Packard and Compaq together, although heirs of HP's founders came out against the deal and worried it would undermine the legendary "HP Way" corporate culture.

And tough times could toughen already solid companies. Even before the height of the crash, Adobe Systems had faced declining revenues and begun restructuring. Losses at Cisco and Sun, among others, were prompts for them to change.

This was Silicon Valley, after all, where failure — even a big failure — is not the black mark it would be elsewhere and where resiliency, adaptability and problem-solving are a way of life. The valley had gone through up-and-down cycles before. This was one more.

First Generation 5 GB iPod

The United States goes to war against the Taliban in Afghanistan.

Code Red worm hits the Internet with the potential to degrade its functioning.

Stem-cell research sparks scientific/ ethical/religious debate.

After 15 years orbiting Earth, the Russian space station Mir was brought back-crashing into the Pacific Ocean.

Outbreak of foot-and-mouth disease in the UK causes British crisis.

BAE Systems is a premier global defense and aerospace company, delivering a full range of products and services for air, land, and naval forces as well as advanced electronics, information technology solutions, and customer support services. BAE Systems has major operations across five continents and customers in some 130 countries. The company employs nearly 100,000 people and generates annual sales of approximately $25 billion through its wholly owned and joint-venture operations.

BAE Systems' Santa Clara facility, which employs more than 1,400 employees, is committed to force protection for both current and future U.S. forces, from vehicle systems to individual soldiers. The Santa Clara facility, once part of United Defense Industries before the company was acquired by BAE Systems in 2005, has a long and rich history in Silicon Valley, dating back to the 1880s, when it was part of FMC. FMC began as the Bean Spray Pump Company before moving into the defense business during World War II. In 1994, FMC merged its Defense Group with Harsco Corporation's BMY Combat Systems to form United Defense, L.P., which was then sold to the Carlyle Group in 1997. United Defense Industries became a publicly traded company in 2001 and BAE Systems is now one of the top 10 defense companies in the United States.

The Santa Clara site is well known for its innovative design and development of the Bradley Combat Systems, the M113 Armored Personnel Carrier, and the Amphibious Assault Vehicle, which provide protection and combat advantage to military troops facing threats around the world.

As a key member of the U.S. Army's Future Combat Systems (FCS) Team, BAE Systems is helping to ensure the future success of U.S. soldiers on the battlefield by developing and demonstrating five Manned Ground Vehicles that are part of the family of systems for FCS, which will include support for the Non-Line-of-Sight Cannon in 2008. These critical systems will be

The fully digital Bradley A3, developed and manufactured by BAE Systems, is the U.S. Army's most advanced combat vehicle system, providing outstanding survivability and mobility to U.S. soldiers in all types of close-combat urban scenarios and in open-combat, open-terrain scenarios. The Bradley fulfills five critical mission roles -- infantry, cavalry, fire support, battle command and engineer squad -- for the Army's Heavy Brigade Combat Teams.

the first in a new line of combat vehicles that will empower soldiers through unmatched firepower, situational awareness, and survivability. BAE Systems' most recent advanced vehicle program -- the mine-protected RG33 wheeled vehicle in 4x4 and 6x6 versions -- is designed to address demanding requirements based on today's threats by delivering enhanced blast protection and survivability to the crew inside. The vehicle series is mission configurable for infantry carrier, ambulance, command and control, convoy escort, explosive ordnance disposal and other roles, and is recoverable by another RG33.

BAE Systems is also developing and delivering integrated survivability technologies, from body armor inserts to advanced armor solutions, that provide new levels of soldier survivability and combat vehicle performance.

Engineers at the BAE Systems facility in Santa Clara are researching, developing and integrating key technologies and capabilities that will be critical to current and future defense equipment using systems engineering and software development processes that are SEI CMMI Level 5 certified.

The Santa Clara facility also is home to the Combat Simulation Integration Lab where vehicle hardware and software tests and evaluation activities are performed and the Power and Energy System Integration Lab, which integrates and tests hybrid electric components and systems.

Through its employees in Santa Clara, BAE Systems is helping to ensure the success and safety of U.S. servicemen and women on the battlefield, empowering them with superior firepower and situational awareness and a new level of advanced survivability solutions.

Chapter 21: The Road Back

iMac G4

Cycles, indeed, are a way of life in Silicon Valley, but the dot-com bubble had been a record-setting high and the burst of the bubble a record low. It would take time to recover.

Throughout 2000, companies retrenched, big companies swallowed smaller ones, and stocks, profits and losses were on a roller coaster ride.

As nervous businesses took an extended breather on information technology spending, times were tough for such corporate software companies as Oracle and Siebel Systems. Companies fought bitterly for what business they could get.

Hopes for an early recovery in personal computers also went unrealized. Processor speeds continued to climb, moving from a top desktop chip speed of 2GHz to 3.06GHz, but such improvements didn't improve sales. Only Apple, which introduced the stylish, flat-panel iMac, created much of a desktop splash. Sales of notebook PCs also showed promise.

Hewlett Packard overcame in-house opposition and won shareholder approval of its absorption of Compaq in May 2001.

Job losses continued as Microsoft trimmed 15,000 workers, Intel 4,000 and AMD 2,000.

And misuse of adware, spyware and PC invasions did little to improve the climate. Spyware began as a seemingly benign marketing tool, but soon became ubiquitous. Pop-ups annoyed Web surfers, spyware invaded their privacy and hackers drained individuals' computer power. Courts and legislators were urged to increase their scrutiny.

By 2003, the technology world was beginning to settle down a bit, though nervousness still abounded. There were some war jitters as the U.S. and coalition forces invaded Iraq to oust the regime of Saddam Hussein.

Western companies began increasing the practice of offshoring, using the less expensive labor in such countries as India, Romania, Bulgaria, Russia, China, Ghana and the Philippines to perform tasks previously handled by American workers. There were predictions that the value of information technology services provided to U.S. businesses from offshore labor would double to $16 billion within one year and triple to $46 billion in three years. A definite trend was under way.

But there were a number of bright spots. Spam, the unsolicited email messages that had been flooding computer users' inboxes, was regulated, first by the European Union, which adopted an "opt-in" directive and then by the U.S. Congress, which passed an "opt-out" bill.

Wireless technology also made huge gains, as Wi-Fi hot spots started to spring up in more and more public places. By the end of 2003, people could feel confident about finding such hot spots in multiple coffee shops throughout most of the world's major cities, allowing them to log on wirelessly to the Internet. Another consumer trend had arrived, fueled in large part by Intel's Centrino chip package, which was tailored for such mobile computing operations.

AMD, meanwhile, introduced its Opteron chip and Athlon 64 processor, helping launch low-cost, 64-bit computing toward prime time by providing

2002

Authorities arrest two gunmen after a wave of sniper attacks in VA, MD and D.C., kills 10.

Accusations of executive misbehavior rock Enron, Arthur Anderson, Merrill Lynch, WorldCom,

Johnson & Johnson, Citigroup and Kmart.

President Bush establishes a Cabinet-level Department of Homeland Security.

2003

U.S. and coalition forces invade Iraq and capture Saddam Hussein.

Space shuttle Columbia explodes on re-entry, kills all seven astronauts aboard.

- 180 -

AMD Opteron 64 processor

faster video encoding, better performance on complex applications like computer-assisted design, and a richer game environment.

By the end of 2003, the Dow Jones Industrial Average had closed above 10,000 for the first time in 18 months and the NASDAQ rose by more than 40 percent from its 2002 levels. Silicon Valley's market for initial public offerings, though improving, still looked anemic with only eight area companies selling shares to the public. Only five companies had gone public here in 2002.

One huge IPO overshadowed all others in 2004. Google, the Mountain View-based search engine, had continued to increase users and add content since its founding six years previous. The company said it had had revenues of $961.9 million in 2003, compared with $238 million for rival Yahoo!, with sales rising 177 percent from a year ago. Google by now had become so popular that its name commonly was used as both noun and a verb. "To Google" something meant to find information about that something quickly. When the company made its initial public offering in August, it was by "Dutch auction" that offered 19,605,052 shares at $85 per share — 14,142,135 of them floated by Google itself and 5,462,917 sold to the public. The sale raised $67 billion and gave Google a market capitalization of more than $23 billion. The vast majority of Google's shares remained under Google's control, and many of its employees became instant paper millionaires.

Intel® Centrino® processor technology

Digital music also became big business, changing the way consumers purchased their favorite tunes. The runaway success of Apple's iPod music player spawned a growing lineup of digital competitors. Apple's iTunes online music store was said to have sold more than 100 million songs, allowing buyers to burn their own CDs and signaling the end of many big bricks-and-mortar record stores.

Internet diarists began attracting increasing attention as the Web gave anyone with a computer a chance to have his or her opinions read. Blogs played a distinctive role in election politics. Dictionary publisher Merriam-Webster named "blog" the most looked-up word on its Web site.

The number of Web users overall continued to increase in 2005, growing by more than 17 million sites and

2004

California voters recall Gov. Gray Davis and elect Arnold Schwarzenegger.

Severe acute respiratory syndrome breaks out in China and kills more than 750 worldwide.

A 9.0 earthquake spawns tsunamis that kill 230,000 people from Thailand to Somalia.

President Bush wins re-election by defeating John Kerry.

Palestinian leader Yasser Arafat dies in a Paris hospital.

Former President Ronald Reagan dies 10 years after announcing that he was suffering from Alzheimer's disease.

- 181 -

topping the previous record of 16 million net sites set at the height of the dot-com boom in 2000. More small businesses were going online and firms were making the most of online advertising.

More people also were using new technology to place telephone calls over the Internet using VoIP (Voice over Internet protocol). Skype, a leading company providing such services, was snapped up by eBay in September, 2005, for $2.6 billion. And continuing advances in technology allowed cellular telephones to go beyond simply placing and receiving calls, expanding their uses to include photographs, video clips, games and mapping. Individuals also increased their personal participation in this wired world by posting audio and, later, video messages on Apple's iPod players and other personal devices, launching a trend known as "podcasting."

Technology was paying big. Executives at Silicon Valley's top 150 companies raked in $2.6 billion in wages and other compensation, reported the *San Jose Mercury News*, which trumpeted the fade of memories of the tech bust. Topping the list was Omid Kordestani, senior vice president of worldwide sales for Google, with $289 million in salary, stock options and bonuses. Second was Terry Semel, chairman and CEO at Yahoo!, with $183 million and Larry Ellison, Oracle's CEO, with $75 million. The Securities and Exchange Commission began looking into companies' use of stock options, proposing increased disclosure and worrying about the practice of back-dating.

Internet entrepreneurship continued to bloom in 2006 with newer sites such as MySpace, Facebook and YouTube displaying huge popularity, especially among younger Web surfers. Facebook, headed by Mark Zuckerberg of Palo Alto, originally was developed as a social networking site for college and university sites, but had grown rapidly after opening itself up to anyone with an email address. Another social networking site, MySpace, allowed users to post blurbs about themselves and say who they'd like to meet, as well as offering links to the users' friends. By August 2006 it was doing such big business that Google signed a $900 million deal to provide a Google search facility and advertising on the site. San Bruno-based YouTube, founded in 2005 by early PayPal employees Steve Chen, Chad Hurley and Jawed Karim, became the biggest deal. The site, where users post and share their own videos, saw such rapid growth in popularity that in October 2006 it was purchased by Google for $1.65 billion in Google stock.

There was a touch of intrigue as Hewlett-Packard found itself in a high-tech whodunit. An internal investigation to find the source of a boardroom leak to media was found to have used an illegal technique known as "pre-texting," which forced the resignation of several

2005

Iraqis vote for a new government in their first free election in a half-century.	*Martha Stewart is released after a five-month prison term, for Illegal behavior in a stock sale.*	*Pope John Paul II dies at 84. Joseph Ratzinger succeeds him taking the name Pope Benedict XVI.*	*Eric Rudolph pleads guilty to the Atlanta Olympics bomb attack.*	*Mark Felt admits to being "Deep Throat," ends years of speculation about this key*	*figure in the Watergate scandal that led to President Nixon's resignation.*

- 182 -

top executives. Overall, though, HP continued to muscle up in the personal computer market under the leadership of Mark Hurd, who had replaced former CEO Carly Fiorina. It was topping rival Dell for market share, an unheard of possibility only a few years earlier.

In the early months of 2007, the *San Jose Mercury News* was proclaiming a wide-scale Silicon Valley rebound. Although 200,000 jobs had been lost here in the tech downturn, 50,000 jobs had been added since 2005 and total employment in the region was more than 1.2 million, nearing the approximately 1.4 million at the height of the boom. Home

values continued to climb. Silicon Valley household income topped an estimated $81,000.

The Silicon Valley index, compiled by Joint Venture: Silicon Network, said that the technology hub had rebooted, shaking off post-crash doldrums.

The number of publicly traded companies in the valley continued to shrink, with the majority of those disappearing by being acquired by others. Maxtor was bought by Seagate. Siebel Systems was bought by Oracle, which announced it also would swallow up Hyperion Systems.

Facebook headquarters in Palo Alto, California.

But the valley's power to generate new startup companies and new technologies remained unabated. A study conducted by Robert Fairlie of the University of California-Santa Cruz found the creation of startups was accelerating. And a study for the U.S. Small Business Administration pointed out that entrepreneurship was higher after the dot-com bust in Silicon Valley than during the boom period.

"The idea that we are an entrepreneurial hot spot is true," said Doug Henton of Collaborative Economics, a Mountain View economic research firm that had conducted the SBA study. "I don't think we've been a large-companies place."

Big or small, Silicon Valley was back.

2006

Hurricane Katrina ravages New Orleans and the South with winds topping 140 mph.

Israel launches a series of raids into Lebanon after Hezbollah forces cross into Israel, kill three soldiers and abduct two more. A cease-fire takes effect a month later.

An outbreak of E. coli bacteria in tainted spinach sickens Americans in 26 states

Former Iraqi leader Saddam Hussein and two other defendants are executed by hanging after being sentenced by an Iraq court.

The largest source of aerial photography has converged resource, talent, technology and the Internet to bring world-class aerial imagery on-line.

ProAerial Video is the largest on-line resource for collecting, cataloguing, displaying and selling stock aerial video footage. They specialize in site-specific imagery with an emphasis on city skylines, recognizable landmarks and landscapes around the globe. By visiting www.proaerialvideo.com one can navigate through a multitude of cities, landscapes, volcanoes and waterfalls – all in real time motion from the air.

ProAerialVideo is the project of aerial videographers and aerial photographers, Julie and Pat Belanger. They are also owners of the 111th Aerial Photography Squadron, which has been specializing in providing the finest still and moving aerial

imagery for their clientele around the world. The Belangers are also members of the Professional Aerial Photographers Association International (PAPA) where Julie is an Executive Director of the organization. This association allowed the Belangers to develop close relationships with colleagues around the globe who have found ProAerialVideo to be the ideal site for displaying and marketing their own stock footage to buyers.

Julie and Pat Belanger

Julie Belanger is a pilot and comes from a flying background. Her family owned the famous Flying Lady Restaurant in Morgan Hill, California, once the world's largest restaurant, seating more than 2000 guests on three levels. The aviation themed restaurant, named for Julie's mother, a pilot, held seven full-sized antique aircraft hanging from the ceiling while more than 100 scale model airplanes "flew" over the heads of the

diners on a moving track. Her family also collected antique aircraft, including a rare 1929 Ford Tri-Motor.

Pat Belanger is an experienced pilot of fixed wing aircraft and helicopters with more than 13,000 hours of flight time. He proudly looks back on his career as an F-16 fighter pilot with the Air National Guard and also as an airline pilot with US Airways.

Chapter 22: Peering into the Future

San Jose City Hall.

How far into the future can the Silicon Valley Renaissance carry? For another generation or two? Another century? For 500 years?

Despite its boom and bust cycles, the valley has maintained its tremendous "installed base" — arguably the world's greatest high-tech aggregation of creative companies, rich in brainpower, financial power, research power and know-how. Supporting them is a robust infrastructure of venture capitalists, specialized law and accounting firms, management consultants, marketing experts, suppliers and specialty service providers.

Looking back at the dot-com bubble, Sun Microsystems CEO Jonathan Schwartz recently waxed philosophical — and optimistic. "I think with any technology that comes out that has the potential to really transform society, there's always the risk that the expectations are going to get a little bit away from at least the immediate results," he said. "So there's an euphoria, called 'the bubble.' But one of the important things to remember about bubbles is that they typically precede build-outs."

There remain numerous avenues for Silicon Valley companies, new and old, to build for the future: nanotechnology, bioscience, "smart" systems applications, creation and use of new materials, expanded robotics, tools for education, tools to wire the world more completely and efficiently than ever before. Development of alternative fuels and alternatives to the internal combustion engine also are becoming increasingly intriguing to the valley's best minds.

It long has been this way. As Valley pioneer David Packard pointed out in his book, *The HP Way*, most of the progress of the 20th century stemmed from scientific discoveries made by the end of the 19th. Since then, high-energy physics research (at SLAC and elsewhere) has discovered that the atom itself contains smaller particles that do not obey the Newtonian laws of physics, he wrote, adding: ". . . with the new understanding of the atom, we can create materials that do not occur in nature-offering a whole new world of scientific opportunity. Everywhere I look I see the potential for growth, for discovery far greater than anything we have seen in the 20th century."

Curtis Carlson, CEO of SRI, would agree with that. "I personally think that this is the most exciting time in the history of science and technology," he said recently. "The Internet is still in its infancy. It's still too slow, it's not ubiquitous enough, and it's not secure enough. We basically have to reinvent the entire Internet. We're about to turn medicine upside down, and the consequence for

David Packard

2007

France elects pro-American Nicolas Sarkozy as president, succeeding Jacques Chirac.	A student gunman kills 32 people at Virginia Tech and wounds many more.	Al Gore urges congressional panels to act on global warming.	Nation mourns President Ford's death.	Nancy Pelosi becomes the first woman Speaker of the House.	Bulgaria and Romania join the European Union.

human health and longevity are just profound. And in the energy technology world, innovations are blossoming, and we're entering a very different period of innovation and energy."

Let venture capitalist Vinod Khosla, a founder of Sun Microsystems, sum it up: "My view of the Silicon Valley formula is very simple: You take the best scientists, the best technologists and entrepreneurs, give them the support system, the risk and a sort of greed, and that mix, which I call the innovation ecosystem, can solve almost any problem."

SLAC 2-mile "gun"

Minimum wage increases to $5.85/hr., up from $5.15.	*An article for the BBC mentions that the Mediterranean Sea has "almost 2,000*	*pieces of plastic per square kilometer of seabed."*	*European light-bulb makers announce a plan to phase out the standard light bulb in eight years.*	*Zimbabwe has the world's highest annual inflation rate, reported to be at 3,700%.*	*Russia resumes the long-range bomber flights that was the practice of the Soviet Union.*

Photo Credits

The Santa Clara Valley Historical Association very much appreciates the courtesy of the sources named below in making the photographs in this book available to us.

In the following credits, the page positions of photographs are designated by this key: TL, top left; TC, top center; TR, top right; ML, middle left; MR, middle right; BL, bottom left; BC, bottom center; BR, bottom right; FP, full page. The abbreviation c/o denotes "Courtesy of."

P. : c/o Symantec Archives
P. 1: FP, c/o Santa Clara Valley Historical Assoc. (hereinafter known as SCVHA)
P. 2: FP, c/o SCVHA
P. 3: FP, c/o Gutenberg Museum
P. 4-5: FP, c/o SCVHA
P. 6-7: FP, c/o SCVHA
P. 8: TL, c/o Palo Alto Historical Assoc. (hereinafter known as PAHA); BR, c/o San Jose Mercury News
P. 9: TR, c/o PAHA
P. 10: TL, BR, c/o PAHA
P. 11: BC, c/o Thomas John Gibbons Images
P. 12: TL, c/o California Room, San Jose Public Library
P. 13: TR, c/o PAHA
P. 14: TL, c/o Abbott
P. 15: TR, BR, c/o Abbott Laboratories
P. 16: BL, c/o Abbott Laboratories
P. 17: FP, c/o Abbott Laboratories
P. 18: TR, BL, c/o Abbott Laboratories
P. 20: TL, BR, c/o PAHA
P. 21: TL, BR, c/o PAHA
P. 22: TC, c/o O.C. McDonald
P. 23: TR, BL, c/o O.C. McDonald
P. 24: TL, CR, c/o Stanford University Archive (herinafter known as SUA); BL, c/o PAHA
P. 25: TL, c/o PAHA; BR, c/o U.S. Navy
P. 26: BL, c/o Cornish & Carey
P. 27: TC, c/o SCVHA
P. 28: TL, c/o SUA; BR, c/o Varian Associates
P. 29: TL, TC, c/o SUA
P. 30: CL, c/o Hewlett-Packard Co.
P. 31: TL, BR, c/o Hewlett-Packard Co.
P. 32: CL, c/o Hewlett-Packard Co.
P. 33: TL, BR, c/o Hewlett-Packard Co.
P. 36: TR, c/o PAHA; BL, c/o Varian Associates
P. 37: TL, c/o SUA; BR, c/o Hewlett-Packard Co.
P. 38: TC, c/o SRI International
P. 39: BR, c/o SRI International
P. 40: TL, BR, c/o SRI International
P. 41: BL, c/o Intuitive Surgical
P. 42: TC, PAHA; BL, c/o Varian Associates
P. 43: TL, Hewlett-Packard Co.; BR, c/o IBM Corp.
P. 44: BR, c/o Varian Medical Systems
P. 45: TR, BC, c/o Varian Medical Systems
P. 46: TC, c/o Varian Medical Systems
P. 47: BR, BL, c/o Ropers, Majeski, Kohn & Bentley
P. 48: TL, San Jose Mercury News; BR, c/o PAHA
P. 49: TR, Ampex Corp.; BL, c/o SUA
P. 50: TR, BL, c/o National Semiconductor
P. 51: TR, BL, c/o National Semiconductor
P. 52: BC, c/o Wilson, Sonsini, Goodrich & Rosati
P. 53: TR, c/o Wilson, Sonsini, Goodrich & Rosati
P. 54: TL, Intel Corp.; BR, c/o SUA
P. 55: TR, BL, c/o San Jose Mercury News
P. 56: TL, MR, BL, c/o Vishay Siliconix
P. 57: TL, MR, BL, BC, c/o Vishay Siliconix
P. 58: TL, c/o Syntex Corp.; BR, c/o Stanford Linear Accelerator Center
P. 59: TL, c/o San Jose Mercury News; BR, c/o Varian

Associates
P. 60: BL, c/o Applied Materials
P. 61: TR, BR, c/o Applied Materials
P. 62: TR MR, BL, c/o Intel Corp.
P. 63: TL, c/o SCVHA; BR, c/o Intel Corp.
P. 64: TR, c/o LSI Corp.
P. 65: TC, BR, c/o LSI Corp.
P. 66: BR, c/o AMD
P. 67: BR, c/o AMD
P. 68: FP, c/o AMD
P. 69: BR, c/o AMD
P. 70: TR, BL, c/o Intel Corp.
P. 71: TL, c/o Nolan Bushnell BR, c/o San Jose Mercury News
P. 72: TR, c/o Apple Computer BL, c/o Margaret Kern Wozniak
P. 73: TL, c/o Tandem Computers Inc.; BR, c/o San Jose Mercury News
P. 74: TR, BL, c/o Margaret Kern Wozniak
P. 75: TL, BL, BC, c/o Margaret Kern Wozniak
P. 76: TC, c/o Komag - Tencor
P. 77: BC, c/o Komag - Tencor
P. 78: BR, c/o Oracle Corp.
P. 79: TL, c/o Oracle Corp.
P. 80: TL, c/o IBM Corp.; BR, c/o Sun Microsystems
P. 81: TR, c/o Adobe Corp.; BL, c/o NASA
P. 82: TC, c/o Lam Research Corp.
P. 83: TL, TC, BR c/o Lam Research Corp.
P. 84: BR, c/o Linear Technology
P. 85: TR, BL, c/o Linear Technology
P. 86: BR, c/o MIPS Technologies
P. 87: TL, c/o MIPS Technologies
P. 88: CL, CR, c/o Adobe Systems
P. 89: TR, BL, c/o Adobe Systems
P. 90: BR, c/o Adobe Systems
P. 91: ML, BC, c/o Adobe Systems
P. 92: TR, ML, c/o E*Trade Financial
P. 93: TR, BR, c/o E*Trade Financial
P. 94: TR, BL, c/o Sun Microsystems
P. 95: BR, c/o Sun Microsystems
P. 96: TL, c/o Sun Microsystems
P. 98: TL, c/o Sun Microsystems
P. 99: TR, c/o Sun Microsystems
P. 100: TR, BL, c/o Symantec
P. 101: TR, BC, c/o Symantec
P. 102: TR, BL, c/o Komag Inc.
P. 103: TR, BL, c/o Genentech, Inc.
P. 104: TC, c/o Maxim Integrated Products
P. 105: TR, MC, MR, BR, c/o Maxim Integrated Products
P. 106: TL, BR, c/o Maxim Integrated Products
P. 107: BR, c/o Maxim Integrated Products
P. 108: BC, c/o Zoran Corp.
P. 109: BR, c/o Zoran Corp.
P. 110: TR, ML, BR, c/o IXYS Corp.
P. 111: TC, BR, c/o IXYS Corp.
P. 112: BL, c/o Atmel Corp.
P. 113: TR, BL, c/o Atmel Corp.
P. 114: BL, c/o Cisco Systems
P. 115: TR, c/o Cisco Systems
P. 116: MR, c/o PMC-Sierra, Inc.
P. 117: TR, BL, c/o PMC-Sierra, Inc.
P. 118: MR, c/o Xilinx, Inc.
P. 119: TC, BL, c/o Xilinx, Inc.
P. 120: ML, c/o NASA
P. 121: TR, c/o Alan Dean Walker, San Jose Mercury News; BL, Lockheed Missiles and Space Co.
P. 123: MC, c/o SCVHA
P. 124: BR, c/o SanDisk Corp.
P. 125: FP, c/o Dino Vournas
P. 126: BR, c/o SanDisk Corp.

P. 127: TC, c/o SanDisk Corp.
P. 128: BL, c/o MIPS Technologies, Inc.
P. 129: BR, c/o Lockheed Missiles and Space Company/San Jose Mercury News.; TL, c/o kernelthread.com
P. 130: BC, c/o SST Inc.
P. 131: TR, BL, BR, c/o SST Inc.
P. 132: TL, TR, BR c/o NVIDIA
P. 133: TC, BL, BR c/o NVIDIA
P. 134: TR, BL, c/o Rambus, Inc.
P. 135: BL, c/o Rambus, Inc.
P. 136: TC, c/o Rambus, Inc.
P. 137: BC, c/o Rambus, Inc.
P. 138: TC, BL, BR, c/o Rambus, Inc.
P. 140: BL, c/o Stephen Edmonds and popcorn.cx
P. 141: TC, c/o Intel Corp.
P. 142: TL, c/o Silicon Graphics Inc.; BR, c/o Industrial Light and Magic, ©1994 New Line Cinemas
P. 143: TL, c/o Palm Inc.; BR, c/o BL, Lockheed Missiles and Space Co.
P. 144: TR, BL, c/o NXP Semiconductors
P. 145: BC, c/o NXP Semiconductors
P. 146: ML, c/o Komag - Tencor
P. 147: TL, c/o Intel Corp.
P. 148: TR, BL, c/o CPI Inc.
P. 149: TR, BC, c/o CPI Inc.
P. 150: BL, c/o Robert C. McLaughlin
P. 151: TC, c/o Robert C. McLaughlin
P. 152: TC, c/o SCVHA
P. 153: TR, BC, c/o SCVHA
P. 154: TR, c/o SCVHA; BL, c/o Amazon.com
P. 155: TC, c/o E*Trade Financial
P. 156: TC, c/o Netscape
P. 157: TC, c/o Rambus, Inc.
P. 158: BR, c/o Ariba, Inc.
P. 159: BR, BC, BL, c/o Ariba, Inc.
P. 160: TR, BL, BR, c/o Covad Communications Group
P. 162: TR, BL, c/o Palm Inc.
P. 163: TR, BL, c/o Palm Inc.
P. 164-165: FP, c/o Palm Inc.
P. 166: BC, c/o Robert C. McLaughlin
P. 167: TC, c/o Robert C. McLaughlin
P. 168: BC, c/o Tyco Electronics
P. 169: TC, BC, c/o Tyco Electronics
P. 170: TR, BL, c/o Cypress Semiconductor Corp.
P. 171: BC, c/o Cypress Semiconductor Corp.
P. 172: TR, BL, c/o Cypress Semiconductor Corp.
P. 173: TL, c/o Conner Peripherals; MR, c/o SCVHA; ML, c/o Cypress Semiconductor Corp.; BR, c/o Adobe Systems
P. 174: TL, c/o ALZA Corp.; MR, c/o SCVHA; BL, c/o Oracle Corp.
P. 175: TL, MR, c/o SCVHA; BL, c/o Oregon State University
P. 176: BR, c/o The Star 11-25-2000
P. 177: TL, c/o Encyclopedia Brittanica Online. 4 Oct. 2007; BR, c/o Apple Computer
P. 178: BL, c/o BAE Systems
P. 179: TL, c/o BAE Systems
P. 180: TL, c/o Apple Computer; BR, c/o www. us.playstation.com
P. 181: TL, c/o AMD Corp.; MR, c/o Intel Corp
P. 182: CL, c/o www.computerra.ru; BR, c/o SCVHA
P. 183: TL, MR, BL c/o SCVHA
P. 184: TR, BL, c/o ProAerialVideo.com
P. 185: TC, MC, c/o ProAerialVideo.com
P. 186: TL, c/o ProAerialVideo.com; BR, c/o SUA
P. 187: BC, c/o Stanford Linear Accelerator Center

Bibliography

Caddes, Carolyn, Portraits of Success: Impressions of Silicon Valley Pioneers, Palo Alto, Tioga Publishing Co., 1986.

Carroll, Paul, Big Blues: The Unmaking of IBM, New York, Crown Publishers, 1994.

Cringely, Robert X., Accidental Empires: How the Boys of Silicon Valley Make Their Millions, Battle Foreign Competition, and Still Can't Get a Date, Menlo Park, Addison-Wesley Publishing Company, Inc., 1992.

Davidow, William H., and Michael S. Malone, The Virtual Corporation: Structuring and Revitalizing the Corporation for the 21st Century, New York, Harper Collins, 1992.

De Forest, Lee, Father of Radio: The Autobiography of Lee de Forest, Chicago, Wilcox & Follett Co., 1950.

Enochs, Hugh, The First Fifty Years of Electronics Research, (The Tall Tree, Vol. 1, No. 9), Palo Alto, Palo Alto Chamber of Commerce, The National Press, 1958.

Freiberger, Paul, and Michael Swaine, Fire in the Valley: The Making of the Personal Computer, Berkeley, Osborne/McGraw-Hill, 1984.

Gibson, Weldon B., SRI Guiding Themes: The Take-Off Days, Vol. 2, Los Altos, Publishing Services Center, 1986.

Gilder, George, Microcosm, New York, Simon & Schuster, 1989.

Ginzton, Edward L., Times to Remember: The Life of Edward L. Ginzton, Berkeley, Blackberry Creek Press, 1995.

Grove, Andrew S., High Output Management, New York, Random House, 1983.

Lowood, Henry, From Steeples of Excellence to Silicon Valley: The Story of Varian Associates and Stanford Industrial Park (booklet), Varian Associates, 1988.

Malone, Michael S., The Big Score: The Billion Dollar Story of Silicon Valley, Garden City, N.Y., Doubleday & Company, 1985.

Malone, Michael S.,The Microprocessor: A Biography, Santa Clara, Telos/Springer-Verlog, 1995.

Morgan, James C., and J. Jeffrey Morgan, Cracking the Japanese Market: Strategies for Success in the New Global Economy, New York, The Free Press (a division of Macmillan, Inc.), 1991.

Morgan, Jane, Electronics in the West: The First 50 Years, Palo Alto, National Press Books, 1967.

Neumann, Peter G., Computer-Related Risks, New York, ACM Press & Addison-Wesley Publishing Company, 1995.

Packard, David, The HP Way: How Bill Hewlett and I Built Our Company, edited by David Kirby with Karen Lewis, Palo Alto, Harper Business, 1995.

Rogers, Everett M., and Judith K. Larsen, Silicon Valley Fever: Growth of High-Technology Culture, New York, Basic Books, Inc., Publishers, 1984.

Santa Clara Valley Historical Association, Video interviews of Silicon Valley inventors, company founders, and others, Palo Alto, 1993-95.

Saxenian, Annalee, Regional Advantage: Culture and Competition in Silicon Valley and Route 128, Cambridge, Massachusetts, Harvard University Press, 1994.

Smith, Douglas K., and Robert C. Alexander, Fumbling the Future: How Xerox Invented, Then Ignored, the First Personal Computer, New York, Morrow, 1988.

Varian, Dorothy, The Inventor and the Pilot: Russell and Sigurd Varian, Palo Alto, Pacific Books, Publishers, 1983.

Williams, James C., "Frederick E. Terman and the Rise of Silicon Valley," Technology in America, 2nd ed., edited by Caroll Pursell, Cambridge, Mass, M.I.T. Press, 1990, pp. 276-291.

Williams, James C., The Rise of Silicon Valley, (booklet), Cupertino, California History Center Foundation, 1993.

Winslow, Ward, "David Packard in His Own Words," Peninsula Times Tribune, Palo Alto, October 20, 21, 22, 1991.

Winslow, Ward, and the Palo Alto Historical Association, Palo Alto: A Centennial History, Palo Alto, Palo Alto Historical Association, 1993.

Wolfe, Tom, "The Tinkerings of Robert Noyce: How the sun rose on the Silicon Valley," Esquire, December 1983.

Index

"The high school that I went to generated three Nobel Prize winners—one is Arthur Kornberg, another one is Jerome Karle, who is from the U.S. Naval Research Labs. Each of us were students of Sophie Wolfe, and each of us sort of points back to her as somebody who had an important influence on the way we developed."

—Paul Berg, Nobel Laureate

"Steve Jobs did something for us all. He kind of broke the age ceiling, the glass age ceiling, if you will, on kids going off and doing things that they shouldn't be doing."

—Scott McNealy, Founder Sun Microsystems

"If Leonardo da Vinci had more time to paint the Mona Lisa it would have been different, maybe better."

—John McLaughlin, Publisher, Silicon Valley: 110 Year Renaissance

"What we were proposing to do in 1976—and that had never been done before—was to take a human gene and put it into a microorganism with the correct coding sequence and make a lot of whatever follows, and in this case, human insulin for treating diabetes."

—Bob Swanson, Founder Genentech

"Faith in oneself is the best and safest course."
—Michelangelo

"I met Woz when I was maybe 12 years old, 13 years old. He was the first person I met who knew more about electronics than I did, so we became fast friends."

—Steve Jobs, Founder Apple Computer

"You don't fail until you quit trying."
—Larry Boucher, Founder Adaptec

"When once you have tasted flight, you will forever walk the earth with your eyes turned skyward, for there you have been, and there you will always long to return."

—Leonardo da Vinci

"There was a bar called the Wagon Wheel where if you wanted to know anything about anything, you just went in the Wagon Wheel, and sat down for a couple of hours."
—T.J. Rodgers, Founder Cypress Semiconductor

"There's a lot to be said about being at the right place at the right time, and essentially, we were there."

—David Packard, Founder Hewlett-Packard

"An invention that I would single out for posterity is the development of optical fibers. I think that's going to be one of the most significant things that ever happened."

—Barney Oliver, Founding Director of Hewlett Packard Labs

"In the technology industry when we think of entrepreneurs, we think of risk takers. We think of people who aren't afraid to fail, and we think of people who really are builders, really trying to build enterprises."

—Larry Sonsini, Founder, Wilson Sonsini Goodrich and Rosati

"We came close to death several times, because we just had no money to do anything."

—Scott Cook, Founder Intuit

"While in college, my professor insisted that light did not bend. I didn't agree and spent the following years discovering that light did bend."

—Dr. Narindar Singh Kapany, Father of Fiber-Optics

"The Internet just allows amazing collaboration. So the idea of online design, the idea of 24-hour, around the world, I'm designing, I'm going to sleep now, Asia is waking up, I'll pass my designs on."

—Carol Bartz, CEO Autodesk

"Entrepreneurs, I think, either are or aren't, and I believe it probably has a lot to do with your upbringing, frustration, and you know, your predisposition to being frustrated."

—Jim Clark, Founder Silicon Graphics and Netscape

"If there's a day when I'm tired and I think about leaving, I would have to feel real good that the people I left behind would feel equally passionate about crushing red tape and bureaucracy."

—Bob Swanson, Founder Linear Technology

"I built a receiving set in around 1913, never having seen a set myself, except as pictures in a magazine. And I built a set, just as happened, got it all together, fiddled around, played with it, and within 10 minutes I heard a signal. If I had not heard a signal, and something had been wrong, and I had worked on this for two or three days and got nothing, probably my career would have been quite different."

—Fred Terman, Father of Silicon Valley